CONSTRUCTIVE
FUNCTION THEORY

INTERPOLATION AND
APPROXIMATION QUADRATURES

I. P. NATANSON

CONSTRUCTIVE FUNCTION THEORY

Volume III
INTERPOLATION AND APPROXIMATION QUADRATURES

Translated by
JOHN R. SCHULENBERGER

FREDERICK UNGAR PUBLISHING CO.
NEW YORK

Library of Congress Catalog Card No. 64—15689

CONTENTS

CONTENTS

CHAPTER I

VARIOUS METHODS OF INTERPOLATION

§1. The Problem

The previous chapters have served to establish a familiarity with the many different methods of constructing polynomials (algebraic or trigonometric) approximating a given continuous function $f(x)$. To these belong the BERN-STEIN polynomials, partial sums of orthogonal expansions of $f(x)$, the FOURIER, FEJÉR, and DE LA VALLÉE POUSSIN sums, and etc. In the present third volume of the book we shall consider yet another method of constructing such approximation polynomials—the *interpolation method*. We are hereby concerned with finding a polynomial which coincides with the function $f(x)$ at certain pre-assigned points (the "interpolation nodes"). If this is to be an ordinary algebraic polynomial, then from a geometric point of view it is a question of passing a parabola of sufficiently high degree through the points $(x_i, f(x_i))$, where the x_i are the interpolation nodes. For this reason, the construction of the appropriate polynomial is referred to as parabolic interpolation. In the first chapter we shall for the most part be concerned with the formal aspect of the procedure. We shall then in later chapters study the behavior of the interpolation polynomial $P(x)$ as the number of nodes increases without bound. If we hereby impose no conditions whatever on the function $f(x)$, then its values at the nodal points (which alone determine the polynomial $P(x)$) will be in no way related to the other values of the function. Hence, an increase in the number of nodes does not in general entail approximation of the polynomial to the function $f(x)$ at the non-nodal points. In order to avoid this, we shall here, as in the first volume of the book, restrict our considerations to continuous functions, although many of the results carry over to the broader class of RIEMANN-integrable functions.[1] In this regard we shall be interested in the question of *uniform* approximation by interpolation polynomials; in addition, we shall also be concerned with the mean approximation of $P(x)$ to $f(x)$.

[1] As is known, the set of points of discontinuity of these functions is quite "sparse" (it always has measure zero).

As we shall see, the continuity of the function is not sufficient to guarantee that the interpolation polynomial actually approximate the function as the number of nodes increases. In the following chapter we will support this assertion with appropriate negative results. If we impose additional conditions on the function $f(x)$, we obtain positive results when the increase in the number of nodal points proceeds according to a suitable rule.

The very same problems arise in interpolating with trigonometric polynomials; this manner of interpolating is more natural when the function to be approximated is 2π-periodic.

§2. The LAGRANGE Formula

Let us consider the following problem: let two sets each consisting of n real numbers

$$x_1, x_2, x_3, \ldots, x_n, \tag{1}$$

$$y_1, y_2, y_3, \ldots, y_n, \tag{2}$$

be given where the numbers (1) are pairwise distinct (we do not require this of the numbers (2)). It is required to find a polynomial of lowest possible degree satisfying the equations

$$L(x_i) = y_i \qquad (i = 1, 2, \ldots, n). \tag{3}$$

To solve the problem it is sufficient to note that for the polynomial

$$l_k(x) = \frac{(x - x_1)\cdots(x - x_{k-1})(x - x_{k+1})\cdots(x - x_n)}{(x_k - x_1)\cdots(x_k - x_{k-1})(x_k - x_{k+1})\cdots(x_k - x_n)} \tag{4}$$

the equations

$$l_k(x_i) = \begin{cases} 0 & \text{for} \quad i \neq k, \\ 1 & \text{for} \quad i = k \end{cases}$$

hold.

Condition (3) is therefore satisfied by the polynomial

$$L(x) = \sum_{k=1}^{n} y_k l_k(x). \tag{5}$$

The degree of this polynomial is at most $n - 1$. There is however no other polynomial $M(x)$ from H_{n-1} which satisfies condition (3); if this were the case, then the difference $L(x) - M(x)$ would be a polynomial of H_{n-1} which would not be identically zero and would possess the n roots (1), but this is impossible. The polynomial $L(x)$ is hence the unique solution of the problem. Formula (5), which represents this polynomial in terms of the x_i and y_i, is called the LAGRANGE *interpolation formula*.

The polynomial $l_k(x)$, which is called a *basis polynomial*, can be written in a more abbreviated form.   If we define

$$\omega(x) = (x - x_1)(x - x_2) \ldots (x - x_n), \tag{6}$$

then

$$(x - x_1) \cdots (x - x_{k-1})(x - x_{k+1}) \cdots (x - x_n) = \frac{\omega(x)}{x - x_k},$$

$$(x_k - x_1) \cdots (x_k - x_{k-1})(x_k - x_{k+1}) \cdots (x_k - x_n) = \lim_{x \to x_k} \frac{\omega(x)}{x - x_k} = \omega'(x_k),$$

whence

$$l_k(x) = \frac{\omega(x)}{\omega'(x_k)(x - x_k)}. \tag{7}$$

If $P(x)$ is any polynomial of H_{n-1} and $x_1, x_2, \ldots, x_n$ are distinct values of its argument, then the equation

$$P(x) = \sum_{k=1}^{n} P(x_k) l_k(x), \tag{8}$$

holds, since both sides of this equation are polynomials from H_{n-1} which coincide at the n points x_i.   In particular,

$$\sum_{k=1}^{n} l_k(x) = 1. \tag{9}$$

Now if $f(x)$ is an arbitrary function defined on the interval $[a, b]$ and the x_i are particular nodal points chosen in this interval, then

$$L(x) = \sum_{k=1}^{n} f(x_k) l_k(x) \tag{10}$$

is the unique polynomial of H_{n-1} which coincides with $f(x)$ at the nodes x_i. Of course, $L(x)$ and $f(x)$ may differ at all points $x \neq x_i$.   The polynomial (10) is called the LAGRANGE *interpolation polynomial for the function* $f(x)$. In order to emphasize its dependence on the function, we sometimes denote it by $L[f; x]$.   Formula (8) then implies

$$L[P; x] = P(x), \tag{11}$$

if $P(x)$ is a polynomial of H_{n-1}.

Now suppose that on its domain of definition $[a, b]$ the function $f(x)$ possesses a finite derivative of nth order.   In this case we are able to construct a useful expression for the difference $f(x) - L(x)$ at the non-nodal points.   For such a point x (which is now to be considered fixed in the interval $[a, b]$) we define[2]:

[2] Since $x \neq x_i$ $(i = 1, 2, \ldots, n)$, $\omega(x) \neq 0$.

$$K = \frac{f(x) - L(x)}{\omega(x)} \tag{12}$$

and

$$\varphi(z) = f(z) - L(z) - K\omega(z).$$

This function is defined on $[a, b]$ and possesses a finite nth derivative

$$\varphi^{(n)}(z) = f^{(n)}(z) - Kn!, \tag{13}$$

since $L(z)$ is a polynomial from H_{n-1}, and $\omega^{(n)}(z) = n!$. It is obvious that

$$\varphi(x_1) = \varphi(x_2) = \cdots = \varphi(x_n) = 0.$$

Moreover, from (12)

$$\varphi(x) = 0.$$

Now according to ROLLE's theorem, in each of the n intervals between the $n + 1$ points $x, x_1, x_2, \ldots, x_n$ there is at least one root of the derivative $\varphi'(z)$; $\varphi'(z)$ therefore has at least n distinct roots.

Repeated application of ROLLE's theorem then yields $n - 1$ (distinct!) roots of the second derivative $\varphi''(z)$ in the $n - 1$ intervals between the n roots of $\varphi'(z)$. By continuing this procedure, we arrive at a root of the nth derivative $\varphi^{(n)}(z)$ which lies between the smallest and largest of the numbers $x, x_1, x_2, \ldots, x_n$. Denoting this root by ξ, we then obtain from (13)

$$K = \frac{f^{(n)}(\xi)}{n!}.$$

Formula (12) now leads to the LAGRANGE *interpolation formula with remainder*:

$$f(x) = L(x) + \frac{f^{(n)}(\xi)}{n!}\,\omega(x); \tag{14}$$

it is hereby of importance that $a < \xi < b$.

Formula (14) affords the simple

Theorem. *If $f(x)$ is an entire function defined on $[a, b]$ and if the number of nodes, which are all assumed to lie in $[a, b]$, is increased without bound according to any rule whatever, then*

$$\lim_{n \to \infty} L(x) = f(x)$$

uniformly on $[a, b]$.

Proof. For any $x \in [a, b]$, $|\omega(x)| \leq (b - a)^n$. If we set

$$M_n = \max |f^{(n)}(x)|,$$

then it follows from (14) that

$$|f(x) - L(x)| \leq \frac{M_n}{n!}(b - a)^n.$$

In Volume I, Chapter IX, § 1 we proved that

$$\lim_{n \to \infty} \frac{\sqrt[n]{M_n}}{n} = 0.$$

From this it follows that

$$\lim_{n \to \infty} \left[\frac{\sqrt[n]{M_n}}{n} e(b - a) \right] = 0,$$

and hence *a fortiori* that

$$\lim_{n \to \infty} \left[\frac{M_n}{n^n} e^n(b - a)^n \right] = 0. \tag{15}$$

Since

$$\frac{n^n}{n!} < e^n,$$

it follows from (15) that

$$\lim_{n \to \infty} \left[\frac{M_n}{n!}(b - a)^n \right] = 0,$$

wherewith the theorem is proved.

§3. A Rearrangement of the LAGRANGE Formula—NEWTON'S Formula

Suppose that we know the values $f(x_1), \ldots, f(x_n)$ of some function at the nodes $x_1, x_2, \ldots, x_n$, and we now wish to find its values at non-nodal points. If the structural properties of the function are nice enough, then—as we already know—the LAGRANGE interpolation polynomial represents the function to arbitrary accuracy when the number of nodes is sufficiently high. Hence in this case it is both natural and justified to set the unknown value of $f(x)$ equal to the known value of $L(x)$.

For example, suppose that $f(x)$ is the steam pressure in a boiler at temperature x. If we measure this pressure at the temperatures $x_1, x_2, \ldots, x_n$ and form the interpolation polynomial we obtain a formula that makes it possible for us to calculate the pressure at unobserved temperatures as well.[3] However, for this example the form (10) of the interpolation polynomial turns out to be unsuitable. For if we subsequently perform still another measurement of the temperature x_{n+1}, we must then change all summands in the sum (10) and carry out all calculations anew. This situation gave rise to the idea, which goes back to NEWTON, of writing the polynomial $L(x)$ not in the form (10), but rather in the form

$$L(x) = A_0 + A_1(x - x_1) + A_2(x - x_1)(x - x_2)$$
$$+ \cdots + A_{n-1}(x - x_1) \ldots (x - x_{n-1}). \tag{16}$$

If we here substitute $x = x_1$, $x = x_2$, $\ldots$, $x = x_n$ in succession and each time make use of $L(x_i) = y_i$ we thus find all the coefficients A_0, A_1, $\ldots$, A_{n-1}. It is immediately obvious that A_{k-1} depends only on x_1, x_2, $\ldots$, x_k and y_1, y_2, $\ldots$, y_k and not on x_i and y_i for $i > k$. Thus introduction of a new node requires the addition of only a single new summand in (16) while all summands already present are retained.

We now develop a formula for calculating A_{k-1}. Since the polynomial

$$L_k(x) = A_0 + A_1(x - x_1) + \cdots + A_{k-1}(x - x_1) \cdots (x - x_{k-1})$$

takes on the values y_1, y_2, $\ldots$, y_k for the arguments $x = x_1$, x_2, $\ldots$, x_k, it may be represented in the LAGRANGE form (5):

$$L_k(x) = \sum_{i=1}^{k} \frac{\omega_k(x)}{\omega_k'(x_i)(x - x_i)} y_i,$$

where

$$\omega_k(x) = (x - x_1)(x - x_2) \ldots (x - x_k).$$

Its leading coefficient A_{k-1} is therefore

$$A_{k-1} = \sum_{i=1}^{k} \frac{y_i}{\omega_k'(x_i)}. \tag{17}$$

It remains only to note that

$$\omega_k'(x_i) = (x_i - x_1) \ldots (x_i - x_{i-1})(x_i - x_{i+1}) \ldots (x_i - x_k). \tag{18}$$

Thus, for example,

$$A_0 = y_1, \quad A_1 = \frac{y_1}{x_1 - x_2} + \frac{y_2}{x_2 - x_1},$$

$$A_2 = \frac{y_1}{(x_1 - x_2)(x_1 - x_3)} + \frac{y_2}{(x_2 - x_1)(x_2 - x_3)} + \frac{y_3}{(x_3 - x_1)(x_3 - x_2)}.$$

[3] Intentionally schematic. In practice direct interpolation is seldom used to obtain an "empirical formula".

3. A REARRANGEMENT OF THE LAGRANGE FORMULA—NEWTON'S FORMULA 13

We now consider more closely the important case in which the nodes form an arithmetic sequence. For this purpose we first define the *concept of differences*. Let

$$y_0, \; y_1, \; y_2, \; y_3, \; \ldots \tag{19}$$

be any finite or infinite sequence of numbers. We define [4]

$$\Delta\, y_k = y_{k+1} - y_k,$$
$$\Delta^2 y_k = \Delta y_{k+1} - \Delta y_k,$$
$$\cdots \cdots \cdots \cdots \cdots$$
$$\Delta^{n+1} y_k = \Delta^n y_{k+1} - \Delta^n y_k$$
$$\cdots \cdots \cdots \cdots \cdots$$

One easily sees that

$$\Delta^2 y_k = y_{k+2} - 2y_{k+1} + y_k,$$
$$\Delta^3 y_k = y_{k+3} - 3y_{k+2} + 3y_{k+1} - y_k,$$

and in general

$$\Delta^n y_k = \sum_{r=0}^{n} (-1)^{n-r} C_n^r y_{k+r}, \tag{20}$$

which can easily be verified by complete induction. The quantities Δy_k, $\Delta^2 y_k, \ldots$ are called differences of first, second, etc. order of the sequence (19).

We now return to formula (16) and choose the interpolation nodes

$$x_1 = a, \quad x_2 = a + h, \quad x_3 = a + 2h, \quad \ldots, \quad x_n = a + (n-1)h,$$

where h is a nonzero number.

In this case

$$x_i - x_r = (i - r)h;$$

hence from (18) it follows that

$$\omega_k'(x_i) = (-1)^{k-i} h^{k-1} (i-1)! (k-i)!.$$

Substituting this into (17), we find

$$A_{k-1} = \sum_{i=1}^{k} \frac{(-1)^{k-i} y_i}{h^{k-1}(i-1)!(k-i)!}$$

or

$$A_{k-1} = \frac{1}{h^{k-1}(k-1)!} \sum_{r=0}^{k-1} (-1)^{k-1-r} C_{k-1}^r y_{r+1}.$$

---

[4] We actually introduce new variables Δy, $\Delta^2 y$, ... starting with the variable y. It would therefore be more natural to adopt the notation $(\Delta y)_k$, $(\Delta^2 y)_k$, ...

Comparing this result with (20), we finally obtain

$$A_{k-1} = \frac{\Delta^{k-1} y_1}{h^{k-1}(k-1)!},$$

and formula (16) thus becomes

$$L(x) = y_1 + \frac{\Delta y_1}{h} \frac{x-a}{1!} + \frac{\Delta^2 y_1}{h^2} \frac{(x-a)(x-a-h)}{2!}$$

$$+ \cdots + \frac{\Delta^{n-1} y_1}{h^{n-1}} \frac{(x-a)(x-a-h) \ldots [x-a-(n-2)h]}{(n-1)!}. \quad (21)$$

This formula is called the NEWTON *interpolation formula*.
   If

$$y_k = f[a + (k-1)h],$$

one also uses the notation

$$\Delta^n y_k = \Delta^n f[a + (k-1)h].$$

NEWTON's formula then assumes the form [5]

$$L[f; x] = \sum_{k=0}^{n-1} \frac{\Delta^k f(a)}{h^k} \frac{(x-a)(x-a-h) \ldots [x-a-(k-1)h]}{k!} \quad (22)$$

If, in particular, $P(x)$ is a polynomial from H_{n-1}, then for any pair of numbers a, h the identity

$$P(x) = \sum_{k=0}^{n-1} \frac{\Delta^k P(a)}{h^k} \frac{(x-a)(x-a-h) \ldots [x-a-(k-1)h]}{k!} \quad (23)$$

holds.

   Example. Let

$$P(x) = \frac{(n-x)(n-1-x) \ldots (2-x)}{n!}, \quad a = 0, \ h = 1.$$

In this case

$$P(a) = 1, \quad P(a+h) = \frac{1}{n}, \quad P(a+2h) = \cdots = P[a+(n-1)h] = 0,$$

and hence

$$\Delta^k P(a) = \sum_{r=0}^{k} (-1)^{k-r} C_k^r P(a+rh) = (-1)^k \frac{n-k}{n}.$$

[5] Here $\Delta^0 y_k = y_k$, $\Delta^0 f(a) = f(a)$.

Therefore

$$\frac{(n-x)(n-1-x)\ldots(2-x)}{n!}$$

$$= \sum_{k=0}^{n-1} (-1)^k \frac{n-k}{n} \frac{x(x-1)\ldots(x-k+1)}{k!}.$$

Substituting $x = n + m$, we obtain the useful identity

$$\sum_{k=0}^{n-1} (-1)^k \frac{n-k}{n} C_{n+m}^k = (-1)^{n-1} \frac{(n+m-2)!}{(m-1)!n!}. \qquad (24)$$

We shall subsequently make use of this identity in a somewhat different form; this is obtained by replacing the index k by $n-k$ and interchanging the roles of n and m:

$$\sum_{i=0}^{m} (-1)^{m-i} \frac{i}{n} C_{n+m}^{n+i} = (-1)^{m-1} \frac{(m+n-2)!}{(m-1)!n!}. \qquad (25)$$

§4. Interpolation with Multiple Nodes

In the preceding sections we have constructed the interpolation polynomial from its values at the nodal points. We now consider the following more general problem. Suppose that we are given the nodes (1) and the numbers

$$\begin{aligned} &y_1, \quad y_1', \quad \ldots, \quad y_1^{(a_1-1)}, \\ &y_2, \quad y_2', \quad \ldots, \quad y_2^{(a_2-1)}, \\ &\cdots\cdots\cdots\cdots\cdots\cdots \\ &\cdots\cdots\cdots\cdots\cdots\cdots \\ &y_n, \quad y_n', \quad \ldots, \quad y_n^{(a_n-1)}. \end{aligned}$$

It is then required to construct a polynomial $H(x)$ of lowest possible degree which satisfies the conditions

$$H^{(r)}(x_i) = y_i^{(r)} \qquad (i = 1, 2, \ldots, n; \quad r = 0, 1, \ldots, a_i - 1). \quad (26)$$

This sort of interpolation was first studied by HERMITE [2].

It is easily seen that the problem has exactly one solution. Indeed, if we set

$$P_i(x) = A_0^{(i)} + A_1^{(i)}(x - x_i) + \cdots + A_{a_i-1}^{(i)}(x - x_i)^{a_i-1},$$

then

$$H(x) = P_1(x) + (x - x_1)^{a_1} P_2(x) + \cdots$$
$$+ (x - x_1)^{a_1}(x - x_2)^{a_2} \ldots (x - x_{n-1})^{a_{n-1}} P_n(x). \quad (27)$$

For the point x_1 is an a_1-fold root of $H(x) - P_1(x)$; differentiating (27) $(a_1 - 1)$ times in succession and substituting $x = x_1$ into the expressions so obtained and into (27), we obtain all the coefficients of the polynomial $P_1(x)$. In the same way we then make use of the equation

$$\frac{H(x) - P_1(x)}{(x - x_1)^{a_1}} = P_2(x) + \cdots + (x - x_2)^{a_2} \ldots (x - x_{n-1})^{a_{n-1}} P_n(x)$$

in order to determine the coefficients of the polynomial $P_2(x)$, and etc. Finally, all the coefficients of $H(x)$ are determined. The degree of $H(x)$ is clearly not greater than $m - 1$ where $m = \alpha_1 + \alpha_2 + \cdots + \alpha_n$. On the other hand, there is no other polynomial $M(x)$ from H_{m-1} which satisfies all the conditions (26), since otherwise the difference $H(x) - M(x)$ would have a total of m roots (taking into account their multiplicities).

It is possible to find a formula which expresses the coefficients of the polynomial $H(x)$ in terms of the values given in the problem; however, we shall not here undertake these general considerations, but rather restrict ourselves to three special cases:

I. If $\alpha_1 = \alpha_2 = \cdots = \alpha_n = 1$ the problem leads to construction of the LAGRANGE interpolation polynomial.

II. If $n = 1$ there is only one node, and the solution to the problem is given by the TAYLOR polynomial

$$H(x) = y_1 + \frac{y_1'}{1!}(x - x_1) + \cdots + \frac{u_1^{(a_1-1)}}{(a_1 - 1)!}(x - x_1)^{a_1-1}.$$

III. If $\alpha_1 = \alpha_2 = \cdots = \alpha_n = 2$ the solution reads

$$H(x) = \sum_{k=1}^{n} y_k \left[1 - \frac{\omega''(x_k)}{\omega'(x_k)}(x - x_k) \right] l_k^2(x) + \sum_{k=1}^{n} y_k'(x - x_k) l_k^2(x); \quad (28)$$

where (as previously)

$$\omega(x) = (x - x_1)(x - x_2) \ldots (x - x_n), \quad l_k(x) = \frac{\omega(x)}{\omega'(x_k)(x - x_k)}.$$

To prove formula (28) we first note that the degree of the polynomial $H(x)$ is not greater than $(2n - 1)$. The equations

$$H(x_i) = y_i, \quad H'(x_i) = y_i' \quad (i = 1, 2, \ldots, n) \quad (29)$$

are also easily verified. For

$$l_k'(x) = \frac{\omega'(x)(x - x_k) - \omega(x)}{\omega'(x_k)(x - x_k)^2},$$

and hence according to L'HOPITAL's rule

$$l'_k(x_k) = \lim_{x \to x_k} l'_k(x) = \lim_{x \to x_k} \frac{\omega''(x)(x - x_k) + \omega'(x) - \omega'(x)}{2\omega'(x_k)(x - x_k)} = \frac{\omega''(x_k)}{2\omega'(x_k)}.$$

The polynomial $q_k(x) = l_k^2(x)$ therefore satisfies the conditions

$$q_k(x_i) = \begin{cases} 0 & (i \neq k), \\ 1 & (i = k); \end{cases} \qquad q'_k(x_i) = \begin{cases} 0 & (i \neq k), \\ \dfrac{\omega''(x_k)}{\omega'(x_k)} & (i = k). \end{cases}$$

From this it follows that for the polynomials

$$A(x) = \sum_{k=1}^{n} y_k \left[1 - (x - x_k) \frac{\omega''(x_k)}{\omega'(x_k)} \right] q_k(x),$$

$$B(x) = \sum_{k=1}^{n} y'_k(x - x_k) q_k(x)$$

the equations

$$A(x_i) = y_i, \qquad A'(x_i) = 0,$$
$$B(x_i) = 0, \qquad B'(x_i) = y'_i$$

hold; this is however equivalent to (29).

We further write formula (28) in the form

$$H(x) = \sum_{k=1}^{n} y_k A_k(x) + \sum_{k=1}^{n} y'_k B_k(x) \tag{30}$$

with

$$\left. \begin{array}{l} A_k(x) = \left[1 - \dfrac{\omega''(x_k)}{\omega'(x_k)} (x - x_k) \right] l_k^2(x), \\[2mm] B_k(x) = (x - x_k) l_k^2(x). \end{array} \right\} \tag{31}$$

Let us now return to the general case. Suppose $f(x)$ is a function defined on $[a, b]$ which has there a finite derivative of order $m = \alpha_1 + \alpha_2 + \cdots + \alpha_n$ where $\alpha_k \geqq 1$.

Now let $x_1, x_2, \ldots x_n$ be nodes lying in $[a, b]$; we put

$$y_i^{(r)} = f^{(r)}(x_i) \qquad (i = 1, 2, \ldots, n; \ r = 0, 1, \ldots, a_i - 1).$$

We can now construct the HERMITE interpolation polynomial in accordance with conditions (26) and then study the difference

$$f(x) - H(x),$$

where x is a fixed point of $[a, b]$ which is not a node x_i.

We now define

$$\Omega(z) = (z - x_1)^{a_1}(z - x_2)^{a_2} \ldots (z - x_n)^{a_n}$$

and introduce the function

$$\varphi(z) = f(z) - H(z) - K\Omega(z),$$

where

$$K = \frac{f(x) - H(x)}{\Omega(x)}. \tag{32}$$

Then

$$\varphi^{(r)}(x_i) = 0 \qquad (i = 1, 2, \ldots, n; \quad r = 0, 1, \ldots, a_i - 1),$$

for x_i is an α_i-fold root of $\Omega(z)$. Moreover, (32) implies that

$$\varphi(x) = 0.$$

The function $\varphi(z)$ therefore has at least $m + 1$ roots in $[a, b]$ (taking into account their multiplicities). From this on the basis of ROLLE's theorem we find at least m roots for $\varphi'(z)$, at least $m - 1$ roots for $\varphi''(z)$, and etc. In particular, $\varphi^{(m)}(z)$ has at least one root ξ. But now

$$\varphi^{(m)}(z) = f^{(m)}(z) - Km!,$$

whence

$$K = \frac{f^{(m)}(\xi)}{m!},$$

and it follows that

$$f(x) = H(x) + \frac{f^{(m)}(\xi)}{m!}\,\Omega(x) \qquad (a < \xi < b).$$

This is the HERMITE *interpolation formula with remainder*. It follows from this formula, in a manner analogous to what was done previously, that the HERMITE polynomials approximate an entire function uniformly when the number of nodes (which may be distributed in any fashion) increases without bound.

§5. Trigonometric Interpolation

Suppose the $2n + 1$ points

$$x_0, x_1, x_2, \ldots, x_{2n} \tag{33}$$

are given in the half-open interval $[0, 2\pi)$. It is then easy to construct a trigonometric polynomial $T(x)$ of lowest possible order which assumes pre-assigned values $y_1, y_2, \ldots, y_{2n}$ at the nodes (33).

Since

$$\sin \frac{x-a}{2} \sin \frac{x-b}{2} = \frac{1}{2}\left[\cos \frac{b-a}{2} - \cos\left(x - \frac{a+b}{2}\right) \right]$$

is a trigonometric polynomial of first order,

$$t_k(x) = \frac{\sin \dfrac{x-x_0}{2} \ldots \sin \dfrac{x-x_{k-1}}{2} \sin \dfrac{x-x_{k+1}}{2} \ldots \sin \dfrac{x-x_{2n}}{2}}{\sin \dfrac{x_k-x_0}{2} \ldots \sin \dfrac{x_k-x_{k-1}}{2} \sin \dfrac{x_k-x_{k+1}}{2} \ldots \sin \dfrac{x_k-x_{2n}}{2}} \qquad (34)$$

is a trignometric polynomial of nth order (it is important that the number of factors of the numerator be even).
Clearly

$$t_k(x_i) = \begin{cases} 0 & \text{for} \quad i \neq k \\ 1 & \text{for} \quad i = k. \end{cases}$$

Hence the polynomial

$$T(x) = \sum_{k=0}^{2n} y_k t_k(x) \qquad (35)$$

satisfies the conditions

$$T(x_i) = y_i \qquad (i = 0, 1, \ldots, 2n). \qquad (36)$$

The order of $T(x)$ is at most n. There can be no other polynomials $M(x)$ from H_n^T which satisfy the given conditions, for otherwise the difference $T(x) - M(x)$ would be a polynomial of H_n^T, not identically zero, which would have the $2n + 1$ roots (33); this however is a contradiction.

Suppose now that $n + 1$ nodes

$$x_0, x_1, \ldots, x_n \qquad (37)$$

are given in the interval $[0, \pi]$; if we put

$$c_k(x) = \frac{\left\{ \begin{matrix} (\cos x - \cos x_0) \ldots (\cos x - \cos x_{k-1})(\cos x - \cos x_{k+1}) \\ \ldots (\cos x - \cos x_n) \end{matrix} \right\}}{\left\{ \begin{matrix} (\cos x_k - \cos x_0) \ldots (\cos x_k - \cos x_{k-1})(\cos x_k - \cos x_{k+1}) \\ \ldots (\cos x_k - \cos x_n) \end{matrix} \right\}}$$

$$C(x) = \sum_{k=0}^{n} y_k c_k(x),$$

then this is an even trigonometric polynomial of degree at most n for which

$$C(x_i) = y_i \qquad (i = 0, 1, \ldots, n). \quad (38)$$

There are no other such polynomials in H_n^T. If $M(x)$ were such a polynomial, then the difference $C(x) - M(x)$ would vanish not only at the points (37), but also at the points $-x_i$. If we order $x_0 < x_1 < \cdots < x_n$, then the difference $C(x) - M(x)$, even in the case $x_0 = 0$, $x_n = \pi$, would have a total of $2n + 1$ nonequivalent roots, while $x_0 = 0$ would be a double root.

Finally, if given n nodes in the interval $(0, \pi)$ one puts

$$s_k(x) = \frac{\left\{ \begin{array}{c} (\cos x - \cos x_1) \ldots (\cos x - \cos x_{k-1})(\cos x - \cos x_{k+1}) \\ \ldots (\cos x - \cos x_n) \sin x \end{array} \right\}}{\left\{ \begin{array}{c} (\cos x_k - \cos x_1) \ldots (\cos x_k - \cos x_{k-1})(\cos x_k - \cos x_{k+1}) \\ \ldots (\cos x_k - \cos x_n) \sin x_k \end{array} \right\}},$$

$$S(x) = \sum_{k=1}^{n} y_k s_k(x),$$

then an odd polynomial of order at most n is obtained for which

$$S(x_i) = y_i \qquad (i = 1, 2, \ldots, n);$$

uniqueness is easily verified here also.

The difference in the number of nodes in these three cases is explained by the fact that complete determination of a polynomial requires the knowledge of all its coefficients. If now

$$T(x) = A + \sum_{k=1}^{n} (a_k \cos kx + b_k \sin kx),$$

$$C(x) = A + \sum_{k=1}^{n} a_k \cos kx, \qquad S(x) = \sum_{k=1}^{n} b_k \sin kx;$$

the number of coefficients occurring in $T(x)$ is $2n + 1$, in $C(x)$ $n + 1$, and in $S(x)$ n. Condition (36) is equivalent to the linear equation

$$A + \sum_{k=1}^{n} (a_k \cos kx_i + b_k \sin kx_i) = y_i \quad (39)$$

for the coefficients A, a_k, b_k. The number of nodes is therefore simply equal to the number of equations required for the determination of the coefficient.s

From the unique solvability of a system of equations of the type (39), it follows moreover that the determinant

$$\begin{vmatrix} 1 & \cos x_0 & \sin x_0 & \cos 2x_0 & \ldots & \sin nx_0 \\ 1 & \cos x_1 & \sin x_1 & \cos 2x_1 & \ldots & \sin nx_1 \\ \multicolumn{6}{c}{\cdots\cdots\cdots\cdots\cdots\cdots} \\ 1 & \cos x_{2n} & \sin x_{2n} & \cos 2x_{2n} & \ldots & \sin nx_{2n} \end{vmatrix}$$

is different from zero if $0 \leqq x_0 < x_1 < \cdots < x_{2n} < 2\pi$. Similarly, the determinants

$$\begin{vmatrix} 1 & \cos x_0 & \cos 2x_0 & \ldots & \cos nx_0 \\ 1 & \cos x_1 & \cos 2x_1 & \ldots & \cos nx_1 \\ \multicolumn{5}{c}{\cdots\cdots\cdots\cdots\cdots\cdots} \\ 1 & \cos x_n & \cos 2x_n & \ldots & \cos nx_n \end{vmatrix}, \qquad \begin{vmatrix} \sin x_1 & \sin 2x_1 & \ldots & \sin nx_1 \\ \sin x_2 & \sin 2x_2 & \ldots & \sin nx_2 \\ \multicolumn{4}{c}{\cdots\cdots\cdots\cdots\cdots} \\ \sin x_n & \sin 2x_n & \ldots & \sin nx_n \end{vmatrix}$$

are likewise nonzero if in the first case $0 \leqq x_0 < x_1 < \cdots < x_n \leqq \pi$, and in the second case $0 < x_1 < x_2 < \cdots < x_n < \pi$. In the repeatedly cited monograph by V. L. GONCHAROV the reader will find the exact values of all these determinants.[6] The case in which the nodes follow one another *at equal distances* is of particular interest:

$$x_k = \frac{2k\pi}{2n+1} \qquad (k = 0, 1, 2, \ldots, 2n). \quad (40)$$

In this case the basis polynomial has the simple form

$$t_k(x) = \frac{1}{2n+1} \frac{\sin \dfrac{2n+1}{2}(x - x_k)}{\sin \dfrac{x - x_k}{2}}.$$

It is then clear that

$$t_k(x_i) = \begin{cases} 0 & (i = k), \\ 1 & (i = k), \end{cases}$$

and the fact that $t_k(x)$ is a polynomial of nth order follows from the formula [7]

$$\frac{\sin \dfrac{2n+1}{2}\alpha}{2 \sin \dfrac{\alpha}{2}} = \frac{1}{2} + \cos \alpha + \cdots + \cos n\alpha. \quad (41)$$

[6] V. L. GONCHAROV [1], p. 43.
[7] Volume I, formula (175).

The interpolation polynomial for the nodes (40) therefore has the form

$$T(x) = \frac{1}{2n+1} \sum_{k=0}^{2n} y_k \frac{\sin \dfrac{2n+1}{2}(x - x_k)}{\sin \dfrac{x - x_k}{2}}, \qquad (42)$$

which is reminiscent of the DIRICHLET integral, and one will note that the behavior of the polynomials $T(x)$ is closely analogous to that of partial FOURIER sums.

We now seek to determine the coefficients A, a_m, b_m in the polynomial (42) by writing it in "canonical form"

$$T(x) = A + \sum_{m=1}^{n} (a_m \cos mx + b_m \sin mx). \qquad (43)$$

To this end, we substitute the expressions for $t_k(x)$ obtained from (41) into (42):

$$T(x) = \frac{1}{2n+1} \sum_{k=0}^{2n} y_k \left[1 + 2 \sum_{m=1}^{n} \cos m(x - x_k) \right].$$

From this it follows that

$$T(x) = \frac{1}{2n+1} \left(\sum_{k=0}^{2n} y_k \right) + \frac{2}{2n+1} \sum_{m=1}^{n} \left[\left(\sum_{k=0}^{2n} y_k \cos mx_k \right) \cos mx \right.$$

$$\left. + \left(\sum_{k=0}^{2n} y_k \sin mx_k \right) \sin mx \right] \qquad (44)$$

and hence

$$A = \frac{1}{2n+1} \sum_{k=0}^{2n} y_k,$$

$$a_m = \frac{2}{2n+1} \sum_{k=0}^{2n} y_k \cos mx_k, \qquad b_m = \frac{2}{2n+1} \cdot \sum_{k=0}^{2n} y_k \sin mx_k.$$

Now if $y_0, y_1, \ldots, y_{2n}$ are the values of some function $f(x)$ at the nodes (40), then the values of the coefficients A, a_m, b_m obtained are nothing but RIEMANN sums for the FOURIER coefficients

$$\frac{1}{2\pi} \int_0^{2\pi} f(x)\, dx, \qquad \frac{1}{\pi} \int_0^{2\pi} f(x) \cos mx\, dx, \qquad \frac{1}{\pi} \int_0^{2\pi} f(x) \sin mx\, dx. \qquad (45)$$

As n becomes large, the coefficients A, a_m, b_m approach the integrals (45), and the polynomial $T(x)$ approaches the FOURIER sum $S_n(x)$ of the function $f(x)$. This is, of course, intended to be only a heuristic consideration and not a precisely formulated theorem.

CHAPTER II

THEOREMS OF NEGATIVE CHARACTER

§1. The Theorems of S. N. BERNSTEIN and G. FABER

Let us consider the following problem: In the interval $[a, b]$ we choose nodes which form an infinite triangular matrix:

$$\left.\begin{aligned}
& x_1^{(1)}, \\
& x_1^{(2)}, \; x_2^{(2)}, \\
& x_1^{(3)}, \; x_2^{(3)}, \; x_3^{(3)}, \\
& \cdots\cdots\cdots\cdots\cdots \\
& x_1^{(n)}, \; x_2^{(n)}, \; x_3^{(n)}, \ldots, x_n^{(n)} \\
& \cdots\cdots\cdots\cdots\cdots
\end{aligned}\right\} \tag{46}$$

Given a function $f(x)$ defined on $[a, b]$, we then construct a sequence $\{L_n(x)\}$ of LAGRANGE interpolation polynomials, where in so doing we use as interpolation nodes in the construction of $L_n(x)$ the n elements of the nth row of the matrix (46), such that

$$L_n(x_k^{(n)}) = f(x_k^{(n)}) \qquad (k = 1, 2, \ldots, n).$$

One then asks the question: Will $L_n(x)$ in this case converge to $f(x)$ at all points of the interval $[a, b]$?

As we already know, the sequence does converge (and even uniformly) for entire functions $f(x)$. It is desirable to avoid such a strong condition. It will now be shown that to every matrix (46) there corresponds a class of functions for which the interpolation process obtained from the matrix converges uniformly.[1] However, this class is always substantially more restricted than the class $C([a, b])$ of all continuous functions on $[a, b]$. In other words, there is no universal matrix (46) which is applicable for all continuous functions. The proof of this fact is the substance of FABER's theorem to which this section is primarily devoted.

---

[1] This class is never empty, since it contains all entire functions (and—trivially—all polynomials).

In studying questions of convergence of the polynomials $L_n(x)$ to a function $f(x)$, the quantity

$$\lambda_n(x) = \sum_{k=1}^{n} | l_k^{(n)}(x)| \qquad (47)$$

plays a major role; here $l_k^{(n)}(x)$ are the basis polynomials of the nth row of the matrix (46), i.e.

$$l_k^{(n)}(x) = \frac{\omega_n(x)}{\omega_n'(x_k^{(n)})(x - x_k^{(n)})} \qquad \left(\omega_n(x) = \prod_{k=1}^{n} (x - x_k^{(n)})\right).$$

The function $\lambda_n(x)$ is the analogue of the LEBESQUE function which we have studied in the theory of orthogonal polynomials.   Putting

$$\lambda_n = \max \lambda_n(x) \qquad (a \leqq x \leqq b), \qquad (48)$$

we formulate

Theorem 1 (G. FABER-S. N. BERNSTEIN).   *For every matrix (46) the inequality*

$$\lambda_n > \frac{\ln n}{8\sqrt{\pi}} \qquad (49)$$

holds.

Proof.   The proof [2] of this important theorem hinges on two lemmas.

Lemma 1.   *Given n arbitrary points $\theta_1, \theta_2, \ldots, \theta_n$ $(0 \leqq \theta_k \leqq \pi)$, there exists an even trigonometric polynomial $T(\theta)$ of order at most $n - 1$ such that*

$$| T(\theta_i)| \leqq 8\sqrt{\pi} \qquad (i = 1, 2, \ldots, n) \quad (50)$$

and which satisfies the inequality

$$T(\alpha) > \ln n \qquad (51)$$

at at least one point $\alpha \, \epsilon \, [0, \pi]$.

Proof.   Let $c_k(\theta)$ be those even trigonometric polynomials of order at most $n - 1$ for which

$$c_k(\theta_i) = \begin{cases} 0 & \text{for} \quad i \neq k, \\ 1 & \text{for} \quad i = k. \end{cases}$$

Further, let

[2] G. FABER [1], S. N. BERNSTEIN [6].   The proof given in the text is due to FEJÉR [3].

$$A(\theta) = \frac{\cos \theta}{n-1} + \frac{\cos 2\theta}{n-2} + \cdots + \frac{\cos (n-1)\theta}{1},$$

$$B(\theta) = \frac{\cos (n+1)\theta}{1} + \frac{\cos (n+2)\theta}{2} + \cdots + \frac{\cos (2n-1)\theta}{n-1}$$

As we already know [3] the following inequality holds for all θ:

$$|A(\theta) - B(\theta)| \leq 4\sqrt{\pi}. \tag{52}$$

Finally, let us introduce the polynomial

$$U(\theta) = A(2\theta) - \sum_{k=1}^{n} [B(\theta_k + \theta) + B(\theta_k - \theta)]c_k(\theta),$$

which is an even trigonometric polynomial. It is easily seen that

$$\int_0^\pi U(\theta) \, d\theta = \frac{1}{2} \int_{-\pi}^\pi U(\theta) \, d\theta = 0. \tag{53}$$

For $A(2\theta)$ is a trigonometric polynomial without constant term which is therefore orthogonal to 1 on the interval $[-\pi, \pi]$. Also, $B(\theta_k + \theta) + B(\theta_k - \theta)$ is a linear combination of terms of the form $\cos m\theta$ with $m > n$; this linear combination is therefore orthogonal to the polynomials $c_k(\theta)$ whose order is less than n.

Hence, there exists a point α in the interval $[0, \pi]$ at which

$$U(\alpha) = 0.$$

With these remarks in mind, we define

$$T(\theta) = [A(\theta + \alpha) + A(\theta - \alpha)] - \sum_{k=1}^{n} [B(\theta_k + \alpha) + B(\theta_k - \alpha)]c_k(\theta).$$

This is also an even trigonometric polynomial from H_{n-1}^T ,[4] and in particular

$$T(\theta_i) = [A(\theta_i + \alpha) - B(\theta_i + \alpha)] + [A(\theta_i - \alpha) - B(\theta_i - \alpha)];$$

therefore, on the basis of (52) it satisfies (50). On the other hand,

$$T(\alpha) = A(0) + U(\alpha) = A(0)$$

or

$$T(\alpha) = 1 + \frac{1}{2} + \cdots + \frac{1}{n-1} > \int_1^n \frac{dx}{x} = \ln n,$$

and hence (51) is also satisfied.

[3] Volume I, inequality (186).
[4] For $B(\theta_k + \alpha)$ and $B(\theta_k - \alpha)$ are constants.

Lemma 2. *Given n arbitrary nodes $x_1, x_2, \ldots, x_n$ in $[a, b]$, there exists a polynomial $P(x) \, \epsilon \, H_{n-1}$ such that*

$$|P(x_i)| \leqq 8\sqrt{\pi} \qquad (i = 1, 2, \ldots, n) \quad (54)$$

and which satisfies the inequality

$$P(c) > \ln n \qquad\qquad (55)$$

at at least one point $c \, \epsilon \, [a, b]$.

Proof. This lemma is easily obtained from the previous one. The substitution

$$\theta = \text{arc cos} \, \frac{2x - (a + b)}{b - a}$$

maps the interval $[a, b]$ onto the interval $[0, \pi]$ and takes the point x_k into the point θ_k. If now $T(x)$ is the trigonometric polynomial whose existence was established in Lemma 1, then the polynomia

$$P(x) = T\left[\text{arc cos} \, \frac{2x - (a+b)}{b - a} \right]$$

satisfies inequalities (54) and (55), where

$$c = \frac{b - a}{2} \cos \alpha + \frac{a + b}{2}.$$

Returning now to the FABER-BERNSTEIN theorem, we note that the polynomial of Lemma 2 can be written in the form

$$P(x) = \sum_{k=1}^{n} P(x_k) l_k(x).$$

From this it follows that

$$|P(x)| \leqq 8\sqrt{\pi} \sum_{k=1}^{n} |l_k(x)|,$$

and therefore from (55) that

$$\sum_{k=1}^{n} |l_k(c)| > \frac{\ln n}{8\sqrt{\pi}}.$$

This holds for arbitrary interpolation nodes in $[a, b]$ and hence in particular for the nodes occurring in the nth row of our matrix. The theorem is herewith proved.

Theorem 2 (G. FABER). *Given a matrix* (46) *the points of which all lie in* $[a, b]$, *there exists a function* $f(x) \in C([a, b])$ *such that the interpolation polynomial formed from the rows of the matrix does not converge uniformly to* $f(x)$.

Proof. The proof is by contradiction. Suppose therefore that there is a matrix (46) which for every function $f(x) \in C([a, b])$ ensures uniform convergence of the interpolation polynomial $L_n[f, x] = L_n(x)$ to $f(x)$. As above, we put

$$\lambda_n(x) = \sum_{k=1}^{n} |l_k^{(n)}(x)|, \qquad \lambda_n = \max \lambda_n(x), \qquad (56)$$

and in particular for $z_n \in [a, b]$ let

$$\lambda_n(z_n) = \lambda_n. \qquad (57)$$

We now construct a continuous function $\varphi_n(x)$ for every natural number n by putting first of all

$$\varphi_n(x_k^{(n)}) = \operatorname{sign} l_k^{(n)}(z_n) \qquad (k = 1, 2, \ldots, n) \qquad (58)$$

and requiring secondly that this function $\varphi_n(x)$ be linear between the nodes $x_k^{(n)}$. In order to define it in the entire interval $[a, b]$, we must still attend to its values in the intervals [5] $[a, x_1^{(n)}]$ and $[x_n^{(n)}, b]$: let the function be constant on both these intervals.

It is clear that everywhere in $[a, b]$

$$|\varphi_n(x)| \leq 1. \qquad (59)$$

Also,

$$L_n[\varphi_n; z_n] = \sum_{k=1}^{n} \varphi_n(x_k^{(n)}) l_k^{(n)}(z_n) = \sum_{k=1}^{n} |l_k^{(n)}(z_n)| = \lambda_n(z_n) = \lambda_n. \qquad (60)$$

We now construct an increasing sequence of natural numbers $n_1 < n_2 < n_3 < \cdots$, where in so doing we choose n_1 such that

$$\lambda_{n_1} > 2 \cdot 2 \cdot 3;$$

this is possible, since according to Theorem 1 the numbers λ_n increase without bound. Since the function $\dfrac{\varphi_{n_1}(x)}{3}$ is continuous, according to our assumption its interpolation process converges uniformly. There therefore exists an index n' such that for all $n > n'$

$$\left| L_n\left[\frac{\varphi_{n_1}}{3} ; x \right] \right| < 1.$$

[5] We number the nodes in the natural order

$$a \leq x_1^{(n)} < x_2^{(n)} < \cdots < x_n^{(n)} \leq b.$$

We now choose an index n_2 such that $n_2 > n'$, $n_2 > n_1$, and moreover

$$\lambda_{n_2} > 2 \cdot 3 \cdot 3^2.$$

The function

$$\frac{\varphi_{n_1}(x)}{3} + \frac{\varphi_{n_2}(x)}{3^2}$$

is then continuous and is less in absolute value than $\frac{1}{3} + \frac{1}{3^2} < 1$. We can

therefore find an index n'' such that for $n > n''$

$$\left| L_n \left[\frac{\varphi_{n_1}}{3} + \frac{\varphi_{n_2}}{3^2} \; ; \; x \right] \right| < 1.$$

We now choose $n_3 > n''$, $n_3 > n_2$ such that in addition

$$\lambda_{n_3} > 2 \cdot 4 \cdot 3^3.$$

Continuing this process, we obtain the desired sequence $\{n_m\}$, where for every index m the inequalities

$$\left| L_{n_m} \left[\frac{\varphi_{n_1}}{3} + \frac{\varphi_{n_2}}{3^2} + \cdots + \frac{\varphi_{n_{m-1}}}{3^{m-1}} \; ; \; x \right] \right| < 1, \tag{61}$$

$$\lambda_{n_m} > 2(m+1)\, 3^m \tag{62}$$

hold.   Making use of the numbers n_m, we now define the function

$$f(x) = \sum_{k=1}^{\infty} \frac{\varphi_{n_k}(x)}{3^k},$$

the continuity of which is obvious.   If we define

$$A(x) = \sum_{k=1}^{m-1} \frac{\varphi_{n_k}(x)}{3^k}, \qquad B(x) = \sum_{k=m+1}^{\infty} \frac{\varphi_{n_k}(x)}{3^k},$$

then

$$f(x) = A(x) + \frac{\varphi_{n_m}(x)}{3^m} + B(x);$$

whence it follows that

$$L_{n_m}[f; x] = L_{n_m}[A; x] + \frac{1}{3^m}\, L_{n_m}[\varphi_{n_m}; x] + L_{n_m}[B; x].$$

According to (61) we have

$$|L_{n_m}[A;x]| < 1. \tag{63}$$

Moreover,

$$|L_{nm}[B;x]| = \left| \sum_{k=1}^{n_m} B(x_k^{(n_m)}) l_k^{(n_m)}(x) \right| \leq \max |B(x)| \sum_{k=1}^{n_m} |l_k^{(n_m)}(x)],$$

and hence

$$|L_{nm}[B;x]| \leq \lambda_{n_m} \max |B(x)|.$$

But now

$$|B(x)| \leq \frac{1}{3^{m+1}} + \frac{1}{3^{m+2}} + \cdots = \frac{1}{2 \cdot 3^m}, \tag{64}$$

and hence

$$|L_{nm}[B;x]| \leq \frac{\lambda_{nm}}{2 \cdot 3^m}. \tag{65}$$

Moreover,

$$L_{nm}[f; z_{nm}] \geq \frac{1}{3^m} L_{nm}[\varphi_{nm}; z_{nm}] - |L_{nm}[A; z_{nm}]| - |L_{nm}[B; z_{nm}]|;$$

hence, according to (60), (63), and (65) we obtain

$$L_{nm}[f; z_{nm}] > \frac{\lambda_{nm}}{3^m} - 1 - \frac{\lambda_{nm}}{2 \cdot 3^m} = \frac{\lambda_{nm}}{2 \cdot 3^m} - 1$$

and from this according to (62)

$$L_{nm}[f; z_{nm}] > m. \tag{66}$$

Hence

$$\lim_{m \to \infty} L_{nm}[f; z_{nm}] = +\infty, \tag{67}$$

and this precludes uniform convergence of $L_n[f;x]$ to $f(x)$ contrary to our assumption.[6]

The FABER theorem shows that for every matrix (46) there exists a continuous function $f(x)$, constructed with the help of the matrix, the interpolation process for which does not converge uniformly. The question if

[6] This method of proof is used very often. I suggest that it be called the method of the "sliding hump."

there is perhaps such a function applicable to all such matrices is then of interest. This question is answered negatively by

Theorem 3 (J. MARCINKIEWICZ [1]). *For every continuous function $f(x)$ there exists a matrix* (46) *such that the interpolation polynomial obtained from it converges uniformly to $f(x)$.*

Proof. If of all the polynomials of H_{n-1}, $P_{n-1}(x)$ is the one of smallest deviation from $f(x)$, then there exists an $(n+1)$-termed TCHEBYSHEFF alternant consisting of the points $y_1 < y_2 < \cdots < y_{n+1}$ at which the difference $P_{n-1}(x) - f(x)$ has alternating sign. Now in each interval (y_k, y_{k+1}) there is a root $x_k^{(n)}$ of the difference in question. We take these roots as the nodes of the nth row of our matrix (46). The polynomial $P_{n-1}(x)$ is then at the same time the interpolation polynomial for $f(x)$ corresponding to the nodes $x_k^{(n)}$, and we have only to show that the polynomial $P_{n-1}(x)$ converges uniformly to $f(x)$.

§2. The BERNSTEIN Example

The FABER theorem states that the interpolation polynomial $L_n(x)$ does not always converge uniformly to $f(x)$. This does not exclude the possibility that the sequence of polynomials $L_n(x)$ converge to $f(x)$ at many (or even all) points. The following example shows that the interpolation process may diverge everywhere with the exception of single points.

Theorem (S. N. BERNSTEIN). *The interpolation polynomial $L_n(x)$ for the function $|x|$ with uniformly distributed nodes in the interval $[-1, +1]$ (such that $x_1 = -1$, $x_n = +1$) converges to $|x|$ at no point of the interval $[-1, +1]$ with the exception* [7] *of the points -1, 0, and $+1$.*

Proof. We prove the theorem for a point x such that $-1 < x < 0$; the case where $0 < x < 1$ is entirely analogous.

We introduce the function

$$\varphi(x) = \begin{cases} 0 & \text{for} \quad -1 \leqq x \leqq 0. \\ x & \text{for} \quad 0 \leqq x \leqq 1. \end{cases}$$

Since $x = 2\varphi(x) - x$, it is sufficient to prove divergence of the interpolation process for the function $\varphi(x)$.

---

[7] For the points ± 1 this is clear, since they are nodal points for every value of n.

We choose the $2n + 1$ nodes

$$x_k = -1 + \frac{k-1}{n} \qquad (k = 1, 2, \ldots, 2n+1) \quad (68)$$

and denote the interpolation polynomial for the function $\varphi(x)$ which corresponds to them by $L_{2n+1}(x)$.

From NEWTON's formula (22) we have

$$L_{2n+1}(x) = \sum_{k=0}^{2n} n^k \frac{\Delta^k \varphi(-1)}{k!} (x - x_1)(x - x_2) \ldots (x - x_k) \quad (69)$$

and from (20)

$$\Delta^k \varphi(-1) = \sum_{r=0}^{k} (-1)^{k-r} C_k^r \varphi\left(-1 + \frac{r}{n}\right).$$

Now for $r \leqq n$, $\varphi\left(-1 + \frac{r}{n}\right) = 0$, and hence

$$\Delta^k \varphi(-1) = 0 \qquad (k = 0, 1, 2, \ldots, n).$$

If however $r = n + i$ $(i = 1, 2, \ldots, n)$, then $\varphi\left(-1 + \frac{r}{n}\right) = \frac{i}{n}$, and hence for $k = n + m$ $(m = 1, 2, \ldots, n)$

$$\Delta^{n+m} \varphi(-1) = \sum_{i=1}^{m} (-1)^{m-i} C_{n+m}^{n+i} \frac{i}{n}$$

or from (25)

$$\Delta^{n+m} \varphi(-1) = (-1)^{m-1} \frac{(m+n-2)!}{(m-1)!n!}.$$

Equation (69) now becomes

$$L_{2n+1}(x) = \sum_{m=1}^{n} (-1)^{m-1} \frac{(m+n-2)!}{(m-1)!n!} \frac{n^{n+m}}{(n+m)!} (x+1)$$

$$\times \left(x + \frac{n-1}{n}\right) \ldots \left(x + \frac{1}{n}\right) x \left(x - \frac{1}{n}\right) \ldots \left(x - \frac{m-1}{n}\right). \quad (70)$$

Here all summands have the same sign (as we shall soon show).   Let

$$-\frac{i+1}{n} < x \leqq -\frac{i}{n}. \quad (71)$$

The product

$$(x+1)\left(x + \frac{n-1}{n}\right) \ldots \left(x + \frac{1}{n}\right) x \left(x - \frac{1}{n}\right) \ldots \left(x - \frac{m-1}{n}\right) \quad (72)$$

has $n + m$ factors. Among thse the $m + i$ factors

$$\left(x + \frac{i}{n}\right), \ \left(x + \frac{i-1}{n}\right), \ \ldots, \left(x + \frac{1}{n}\right), \ x, \ \left(x - \frac{1}{n}\right), \ \ldots, \ \left(x - \frac{m-1}{n}\right)$$

are negative, and the rest are positive. The sign of the product is therefore $(-1)^{m+i}$. Therefore, all the summands in (70) have the same sign; the absolute value of this sum is therefore greater than the absolute value of the last summand, i.e.

$$|L_{2n+1}(x)| \geqq \frac{\left| (x+1)\left(x + 1 - \frac{1}{n}\right) \ldots \left(x - \frac{n-1}{n}\right) \right|}{2(2n-1)(n!)^2} n^{2n}.$$

From (71)

$$x = -\frac{i}{n} - \frac{\theta_n}{n} \qquad\qquad (0 \leqq \theta_n < 1),$$

so that we obtain

$$|L_{2n+1}(x)| \geqq \frac{n^{2n}}{2(2n-1)(n!)^2} \left(\frac{n-i}{n} - \frac{\theta_n}{n}\right)\left(\frac{n-i-1}{n} - \frac{\theta_n}{n}\right)$$
$$\ldots \left(\frac{1}{n} - \frac{\theta_n}{n}\right)\frac{\theta_n}{n}\left(\frac{1}{n} + \frac{\theta_n}{n}\right) \ldots \left(\frac{n+i-1}{n} + \frac{\theta_n}{n}\right).$$

The righthand side of this inequality becomes no greater if we replace θ_n by 1 in the first $n - i - 1$ factors and by zero in the last $n + i - 1$ factors. Hence

$$|L_{2n+1}(x)| \geqq \frac{(n-i-1)!(n+i-1)!}{2(2n-1)(n!)^2} \theta_n(1 - \theta_n).$$

Let us examine the factor

$$\sigma_n = \frac{(n-i-1)!(n+i-1)!}{2(2n-1)(n!)^2}$$

more closely.

It is clear that

$$\sigma_n = \frac{1}{4n-2} \frac{1}{n-1} \frac{1}{n}\left(1 + \frac{i+1}{n-i}\right)\left(1 + \frac{i+1}{n-i+1}\right) \ldots \left(1 + \frac{i+1}{n-2}\right)$$

Of the $i - 1$ terms in parentheses the last is the smallest. Hence

$$\sigma_n > \frac{1}{4n^3}\left(1 + \frac{i+1}{n-2}\right)^{i-1}.$$

But from (71)

$$\frac{i+1}{n-2} > -x, \quad i-1 > -nx-2,$$

so that

$$\sigma_n > \frac{1}{4n^3}(1-x)^{-nx-2}, \tag{73}$$

whence it follows that

$$\lim_{n\to\infty} \sigma_n = +\infty. \tag{74}$$

Until now n was an arbitrary natural number. We now make a special choice for it. To this end we fix a number q which satisfies the condition

$$0 < q < \frac{1+x}{2}.$$

Then for every natural number i the length of the interval $\left(\dfrac{i+q}{-x}, \dfrac{i+1-q}{-x}\right)$

is greater than one so that it contains at least one natural number n:

$$\frac{i+q}{-x} < n < \frac{i+1-q}{-x}.$$

For this number n (which by appropriate choice of i can be made arbitrarily large)

$$\frac{i}{n} + \frac{q}{n} < -x < \frac{i+1}{n} - \frac{q}{n},$$

whence

$$\theta_n > q, \quad 1 - \theta_n > q$$

and finally

$$|L_{2n+1}(x)| > q^2 \sigma_n.$$

This in conjunction with (74) completes the proof of the theorem.

Addendum. *The interpolation process of the theorem converges to the function* $|x|$ *at the point* $x = 0$.

Proof. If the number of nodes is odd, then the point $x = 0$ is itself a node. If the number of nodes is even and equal to $2n$:

$$x_k = -1 + \frac{2(k-1)}{2n-1} \qquad (k = 1, 2, \ldots, 2n),$$

and then the LAGRANGE interpolation polynomial corresponding to these nodes is

$$L_{2n}(x) = \sum_{k=1}^{2n} |x_k| \frac{(x - x_1) \ldots (x - x_{k-1})(x - x_{k+1}) \ldots (x - x_{2n})}{(x_k - x_1) \ldots (x_k - x_{k-1})(x_k - x_{k+1}) \ldots (x_k - x_{2n})} ;$$

hence

$$|L_{2n}(0)| \leqq \sum_{k=1}^{2n} \frac{|x_1 x_2 x_3 \ldots x_{2n}|}{|x_k - x_1| \ldots |x_k - x_{k-1}| \; |x_k - x_{k+1}| \ldots |x_k - x_{2n}|}.$$

Noting that

$$x_k - x_i = \frac{2(k - i)}{2n - 1},$$

we find

$$|L_{2n}(0)| \leqq |x_1 x_2 \ldots x_{2n}| \sum_{k=1}^{2n} \frac{(2n - 1)^{2n-1}}{2^{2n-1}(k - 1)!(2n - k)!}.$$

On the other hand

$$|x_1 x_2 \ldots x_{2n}| = \frac{[(2n - 1)!!]^2}{(2n - 1)^{2n}},$$

and hence

$$|L_{2n}(0)| \leqq \frac{[(2n - 1)!!]^2}{2^{2n-1}(2n - 1)} \sum_{k=1}^{2n} \frac{1}{(k - 1)!(2n - k)!}$$

or equivalently

$$|L_{2n}(0)| \leqq \frac{[(2n - 1)!!]^2}{2^{2n-1}(2n)!(2n - 1)} \sum_{k=1}^{2n} k C_{2n}^k.$$

From STIRLING's formula [8]

$$n! = \sqrt{2\pi n}\, n^n e^{-n}(1 + \omega_n) \qquad (\lim \omega_n = 0)$$

we have

$$\frac{[(2n - 1)!!]^2}{(2n)!} = \frac{(2n)!}{[(2n)!!]^2} = \frac{(2n)!}{2^{2n}(n!)^2} = \frac{1 + \lambda_n}{\sqrt{\pi n}} \qquad (\lim \lambda_n = 0).$$

[8] The proof of this formula can be found in Appendix 1 at the end of the book.

Finally, differentiating the identity

$$\sum_{k=0}^{2n} C_{2n}^k x^k = (1 + x)^{2n}.$$

and setting $x = 1$, we find

$$\sum_{k=1}^{2n} k C_{2n}^k = n2^{2n}.$$

Therefore

$$|L_{2n}(0)| \leqq \frac{2n}{2n - 1} \frac{1 + \lambda_n}{\sqrt{\pi n}}, \tag{75}$$

and hence $\lim_{n \to \infty} L_{2n}(0) = 0$.

Remark. S. N. BERNSTEIN did not investigate the case of $x = 0$. The convergence of the interpolation process in this case was first noted in the thesis of D. L. BERMANN. S. M. LOSINSKI proved that the inequality

$$|L_{2n}(0)| < \frac{A}{n},$$

holds, which is stronger than (75). The LOSINSKI inequality follows from the equation

$$L_{2n}(0) = \left[\frac{(2n - 3)!!}{2^{n-1}(n - 1)!} \right]^2,$$

the proof of which we shall not undertake here.

§3. An Example Due to MARCINKIEWICZ

As we already know, the divergence of an interpolation process occurs because the sequence of functions $\{\lambda_n(x)\}$ is unbounded. When the nodes are equidistant, the inequality

$$|L_{2n+1}(x)| > \frac{q^2}{4n} (1 - x)^{-nx-2} \qquad (x < 0)$$

holds at least for arbitrarily many values of n if not for all such values. If we note that the function $\varphi(x)$ for which we constructed the polynomial $L_{2n+1}(x)$ is in absolute value not greater than one, then clearly for all n the estimate

$$|L_{2n+1}(x)| \leqq \lambda_{2n+1}(x)$$

holds.

The function $\lambda_n(x)$ for equally spaced nodes therefore increases faster (at least for infinitely many n) than the general term of a geometric series. It is just this exceptionally rapid increase in $\lambda_n(x)$ which occasions divergence of the interpolation process even for such a "well-behaved" function as $|x|$. It is therefore only natural to ask if there exist continuous functions for which the interpolation process diverges in spite of but slow increase in $\lambda_n(x)$. From the FABER-BERNSTEIN theorem it follows that $\lambda_n(x)$ never increases more slowly than $\ln n$. On the other hand, we will see later that for the TCHEBYSHEFF nodes

$$x_k^{(n)} = \cos \frac{2k-1}{2n}\pi \qquad (k = 1, 2, \ldots, n) \quad (76)$$

the function $\lambda_n(x)$ does not increase faster than $\ln n$. From this point of view the nodes (76) seem to be the best possible. In spite of all this, we will be able to prove the existence of a continuous function for which the interpolation process diverges everywhere even with the nodes (76).

Continuous functions of this type were found independently by J. MARCINKIEWICZ [2] and G. GRUNWALD [1]. We give here — with minor changes— the construction due to MARCINKIEWICZ. GRUNWALD'S example can be found in the book by J. S. BESIKOVICH.[9]

Lemma 1. *Corresponding to every natural number n we define two sets of numbers:*

$$A(n) = \left\{ \frac{1}{n}, \ \frac{3}{n}, \ \ldots, \ \frac{2n-1}{n} \right\},$$

$$B(n) = \left\{ \frac{1}{n+1}, \ \frac{3}{n+1}, \ \ldots, \ \frac{2n+1}{n+1} \right\}.$$

Then the intersection $A(n)B(n)$ is empty. If further S is any finite set of rational numbers from the interval $(0, 2)$, then there exist arbitrarily large values of n for which $A(n)S$ is empty, while the intersection $B(n)S$ is either also empty or contains only the number 1.

Proof. The first assertion is obviously correct.[9] Now suppose that S consists of irreducible fractions $\dfrac{p_i}{q_i}$ $(i = 1, 2, \ldots, s)$. We then set

[9] J. S. BESIKOVICH [1], pp. 168–180.

[9] Suppose $\dfrac{2k-1}{n} = \dfrac{2i-1}{n+1}$, then $\left(1 + \dfrac{1}{n}\right)(2k-1) = 2i-1$. Thus $\dfrac{2k-1}{n}$ would be a whole number and n would be odd; but now $\dfrac{2i-1}{n+1}$ cannot be a whole number.

$$n = 2mq_1q_2 \ldots q_s,$$

where m is a natural number.   If now

$$\frac{p_i}{q_i} = \frac{2k - 1}{n},$$

then this would imply that

$$2mp_iq_1 \ldots q_{i-1}q_{i+1} \ldots q_s = 2k - 1$$

which is impossible.   Hence $A(n)S$ is empty.

If on the other hand

$$\frac{p_i}{q_i} = \frac{2k - 1}{n + 1},$$

then

$$2mp_iq_1 \ldots q_{i-1}q_{i+1} \ldots q_s + \frac{p_i}{q_i} = 2k - 1.$$

Hence $\dfrac{p_i}{q_i}$ must be a whole number, i.e. $\dfrac{p_i}{q_i} = 1$.

We have now only to note that n becomes arbitrarily large with m.

We now denote by $L_n[f; x]$ the interpolation polynomial which coincides with $f(x)$ at the nodes (76).   This polynomial has the form

$$L_n[f; x] = \sum_{k=1}^{n} f(x_k^{(n)}) \frac{T_n(x)}{T_n'(x_k^{(n)})(x - x_k^{(n)})}, \tag{77}$$

where [10] $T_n(x) = \cos(n \text{ arc cos } x)$.   Now

$$T_n'(x) = n \frac{\sin(n \text{ arc cos } x)}{\sqrt{1 - x^2}} ;$$

if we put $x = \cos\theta$ $(0 \leqq \theta \leqq \pi)$ and $\theta_k = \dfrac{2k - 1}{2n}\pi$ $(k = 1, 2, \ldots, n)$, then

we obtain

$$L_n[f; x] = \frac{1}{n}\sum_{k=1}^{n}(-1)^{k+1}f(x_k^{(n)}) \frac{\cos n\theta}{\cos\theta - \cos\theta_k} \sin\theta_k. \tag{78}$$

[10] Strictly speaking, one should set $\omega(x) = T_n(x)$ in agreement with (6).   However, only the relative magnitude $\dfrac{\omega(x)}{\omega'(x_k)}$ occurs in the LAGRANGE formula; it is therefore permitted to multiply $\omega(x)$ by any constant factor.

Lemma 2. *For every k in the sequence $1, 2, \ldots, n$ the inequality*

$$\frac{1}{n} \left| \frac{\cos n\theta}{\cos \theta - \cos \theta_k} \right| \sin \theta_k \leqq 2$$

holds.

Proof. To be more precise we require that $\theta \neq \theta_k$. Since $\cos n\theta_k = 0$,

$$|\cos n\theta| = |\cos n\theta - \cos n\theta_k| \leqq 2 \left| \sin \frac{n(\theta_k - \theta)}{2} \right|.$$

Hence

$$\frac{|\cos n\theta|}{|\cos \theta - \cos \theta_k|} \sin \theta_k \leqq \frac{2 \left| \sin \dfrac{n(\theta_k - \theta)}{2} \right| \sin \theta_k}{2 \sin \dfrac{\theta_k + \theta}{2} \left| \sin \dfrac{\theta_k - \theta}{2} \right|} \leqq n \frac{\sin \theta_k}{\sin \dfrac{\theta_k + \theta}{2}},$$

since $|\sin nx| \leqq n |\sin x|$.

Now

$$\frac{\sin \theta_k}{\sin \dfrac{\theta_k + \theta}{2}} \leqq \frac{\sin \theta_k + \sin \theta}{\sin \dfrac{\theta_k + \theta}{2}} = 2 \cos \frac{\theta_k - \theta}{2} \leqq 2,$$

wherewith the lemma is proved.

Lemma 3. *Let $\varphi(x)$ be a continuous function defined on the interval $[a, b]$, and let $x_1 < x_2 < \cdots < x_n$ be distinct points of this interval. Then given $\varepsilon > 0$, there exists a polynomial $R(x)$ such that* [11]

$$R(x_k) = \varphi(x_k) \qquad (k = 1, 2, \ldots, n), \qquad (79)$$

$$|R(x) - \varphi(x)| < \varepsilon \qquad (a \leqq x \leqq b). \qquad (80)$$

Proof. If

$$q = \min (x_{k+1} - x_k) \qquad (k = 1, 2, \ldots, n - 1)$$

and

$$Q = 1 + n \left(\frac{b - a}{q} \right)^{n-1},$$

then the WEIERSTRASS theorem affords a polynomial $P(x)$ such that

$$|P(x) - \varphi(x)| < \frac{\varepsilon}{Q}.$$

[11] We point out that the lemma says nothing about the degree of this polynomial.

Now let

$$\rho_k = P(x_k) - \varphi(x_k).$$

Putting

$$\rho(x) = \sum_{k=1}^{n} \frac{(x - x_1) \ldots (x - x_{k-1})(x - x_{k+1}) \ldots (x - x_n)}{(x_k - x_1) \ldots (x_k - x_{k-1})(x_k - x_{k+1}) \ldots (x_k - x_n)} \rho_k,$$

then clearly

$$\rho(x_k) = \rho_k, \qquad |\rho(x)| < \frac{\varepsilon}{Q} n \left(\frac{b-a}{q}\right)^{n-1}.$$

The polynomial

$$R(x) = P(x) - \rho(x)$$

therefore satisfies conditions (79) and (80).

Lemma 4. *Let $p > 2$ be a natural number. Then there exists a polynomial $R_p(x)$ satisfying the inequality*

$$|R_p(x)| \leqq 2 \qquad\qquad (-1 \leqq x \leqq 1) \quad (81)$$

which has moreover the property that for any x in the interval $\left[-\cos\dfrac{\pi}{p}, \cos\dfrac{\pi}{p} \right]$ it is possible to find an index $n = n(x) > p$ such that

$$|L_n[R_p; x]| > p. \qquad\qquad (82)$$

Proof. Let m be a natural number which we shall subsequently specify more precisely; for the time being let m satisfy the condition $m > p$.

We denote by S_n the set of all nodes $\{x_k^{(n)}\}$ $(k = 1, 2, \ldots, n)$ and by $S_n(a)$ the set of all nodes lying in the interval $[-1, \cos a]$. From Lemma 1 $S_n S_{n+1}$ is empty.

We now put $n_1 = m$ and define a function $\varphi(x)$ on the set $S_{n_1} + S_{n_1+1}$ by

$$\varphi(x_k^{(n_1)}) = \begin{cases} 0, & \text{if } x_k^{(n_1)} \,\epsilon\, S_{n_1} - S_{n_1}\!\left(\dfrac{\pi}{m}\right), \\[3mm] (-1)^{k-1}, & \text{if } x_k^{(n_1)} \,\epsilon\, S_{n_1}\!\left(\dfrac{\pi}{m}\right); \end{cases}$$

$$\varphi(x_k^{(n_1+1)}) = \begin{cases} 0, & \text{if } x_k^{(n_1+1)} \,\epsilon\, S_{n_1+1} - S_{n_1+1}\!\left(\dfrac{\pi}{m}\right) \\[3mm] (-1)^{k-1}, & \text{if } x_k^{(n_1+1)} \,\epsilon\, S_{n_1+1}\!\left(\dfrac{\pi}{m}\right). \end{cases}$$

Using Lemma 1, we then determine an index $n_2 > n_1$ for which the intersection $(S_{n_2} + S_{n_2+1})(S_{n_1} + S_{n_1+1})$ is either empty or contains the single element $0 = \cos\dfrac{\pi}{2}$. We now define our function $\varphi(x)$ at points of the set $S_{n_2} + S_{n_2+1}$ (with the exception of the point $x = 0$ in case it is already defined there) as follows:

$$\varphi(x_k^{(n_2)}) = \begin{cases} 0, & \text{if } x_k^{(n_2)} \, \epsilon \, S_{n_2} - S_{n_2}\left(\dfrac{2\pi}{m}\right), \\[2ex] (-1)^{k-1}, & \text{if } x_k^{(n_2)} \, \epsilon \, S_{n_2}\left(\dfrac{2\pi}{m}\right); \end{cases}$$

$$\varphi(x_k^{(n_2+1)}) = \begin{cases} 0, & \text{if } x_k^{(n_2+1)} \, \epsilon \, S_{n_2+1} - S_{n_2+1}\left(\dfrac{2\pi}{m}\right), \\[2ex] (-1)^{k-1}, & \text{if } x_k^{(n_2+1)} \, \epsilon \, S_{n_2+1}\left(\dfrac{2\pi}{m}\right). \end{cases}$$

We now suppose that the numbers $n_1 < n_2 < \cdots < n_{i-1}$ with $i < m$ have been determined. We then choose n_i such that the set $S_{n_i} + S_{n_i+1}$ has either no point or at most the point $x = 0$ in common with the set

$$\sum_{k=1}^{i-1} (S_{n_k} + S_{n_k+1});$$

we now define the function $\varphi(x)$ at the points of $S_{n_i} + S_{n_i+1}$ (excepting the point $x = 0$ in case it is already defined there) by requiring

$$\varphi(x_k^{(n_i)}) = \begin{cases} 0, & \text{if } x_k^{(n_i)} \, \epsilon \, S_{n_i} - S_{n_i}\left(\dfrac{i\pi}{m}\right), \\[2ex] (-1)^{k-1}, & \text{if } x_k^{(n_i)} \, \epsilon \, S_{n_i}\left(\dfrac{i\pi}{m}\right); \end{cases}$$

$$\varphi(x_k^{(n_i+)}) = \begin{cases} 0, & \text{if } x_k^{(n_i+1)} \, \epsilon \, S_{n_i+1} - S_{n_i+1}\left(\dfrac{i\pi}{m}\right), \\[2ex] (-1)^{k-1}, & \text{if } x_k^{(n_i+1)} \, \epsilon \, S_{n_i+1}\left(\dfrac{i\pi}{m}\right). \end{cases}$$

In this manner we obtain $m - 1$ numbers $n_1, n_2, \ldots, n_{m-1}$ and a function $\varphi(x)$ defined at all points of the set

$$\sum_{i=1}^{m-1} (S_{n_i} + S_{n_i+1}). \tag{83}$$

We finally define the function $\varphi(x)$ on the entire interval $[-1, +1]$ by setting $\varphi(-1) = \varphi(+1) = 0$ and requiring that it be linear between all points at which it is already defined.   It is then evident first of all that $|\varphi(x)| \leqq 1$.   According to Lemma 3 there exists a polynomial $R(x)$ which coincides with $\varphi(x)$ on the set (83) and which satisfies the condition $|R(x) - \varphi(x)| < 1$ on the entire interval $[-1, +1]$.   It is clear that $|R(x)| < 2$ on the entire interval.

Now let $-\cos\dfrac{\pi}{p} \leqq x \leqq \cos\dfrac{\pi}{p}$, which with $\theta = \arccos x$ becomes $\dfrac{\pi}{p} \leqq \theta \leqq \pi - \dfrac{\pi}{p}$.   We then define an integer i by the requirement $\dfrac{i-1}{m}\pi \leqq \theta \leqq \dfrac{i}{m}\pi$ and investigate the polynomials $L_{n_i}[R; x]$ and $L_{n_i+1}[R; x]$.   If then r is the smallest value k such that

$$\frac{i}{m}\pi \leqq \theta_k^{(n_i)}, \qquad \left(\theta_k^{(n)} = \frac{2k-1}{2n}\pi\right)$$

then from (78) we obtain

$$L_{n_i}[R; x] = \frac{\cos n_i\theta}{n_i} \sum_{k=r}^{n_i} \frac{\sin\theta_k^{(n_i)}}{\cos\theta - \cos\theta_k^{(n_i)}} + \alpha(i). \tag{84}$$

Here $\alpha(i) = 0$ if the point $x = 0$ is not a nodal point $x_k^{(n_i)}$; otherwise it is possible that $\alpha(i) \neq 0$; we can however (on the basis of Lemma 2) be assured that $|\alpha(i)| \leqq 4$.

We now study the individual summands of the righthand side, whereby we drop the index i for brevity.   The function

$$\frac{\sin x}{\cos\theta - \cos x}$$

is decreasing in the interval (θ, π), since its derivative is

$$\frac{\cos\theta\cos x - 1}{(\cos\theta - \cos x)^2} \leqq 0.$$

For $\theta_k \leqq x \leqq \theta_{k+1}$ therefore

$$\frac{\sin\theta_k}{\cos\theta - \cos\theta_k} \geqq \frac{\sin x}{\cos\theta - \cos x};$$

from this it follows that

$$\frac{\pi}{n}\frac{\sin\theta_k}{\cos\theta - \cos\theta_k} > \int_{\theta_k}^{\theta_{k+1}} \frac{\sin x}{\cos\theta - \cos x}\,dx$$

$$(k = r, r+1, \ldots, n-1).$$

Moreover

$$\frac{\pi}{2n}\frac{\sin\theta_n}{\cos\theta-\cos\theta_n} > \int_{\theta_n}^{\pi}\frac{\sin x}{\cos\theta-\cos x}\,dx.$$

Hence

$$\frac{\pi}{n}\sum_{k=r}^{n}\frac{\sin\theta_k}{\cos\theta-\cos\theta_k} > \int_{\theta_r}^{\pi}\frac{\sin x}{\cos\theta-\cos x}\,dx,$$

or

$$\frac{1}{n}\sum_{k=r}^{n}\frac{\sin\theta_k}{\cos\theta-\cos\theta_k} > \frac{1}{\pi}\ln\frac{1+\cos\theta}{\cos\theta-\cos\theta_r}.$$

But now $\cos\theta \geqq -\cos\dfrac{\pi}{p}$.   On the other hand

$$\cos\theta-\cos\theta_r \leqq \theta_r-\theta = \left(\theta_r-\frac{i}{m}\pi\right)+\left(\frac{i}{m}\pi-\theta\right) < \frac{\pi}{n}+\frac{\pi}{m} \leqq \frac{2\pi}{m}.$$

Thus we have

$$\frac{1}{n}\sum_{k=r}^{n}\frac{\sin\theta_k}{\cos\theta-\cos\theta_k} > \frac{1}{\pi}\ln\left(\frac{1-\cos\dfrac{\pi}{p}}{2\pi}m\right).$$

Until now we have not specified the choice of m precisely. We now choose m so large that the righthand side of the last inequality becomes greater than

$$p^2+4p.$$

Then from (84)

$$|L_{n_i}[R;x]| > (p^2+4p)|\cos n_i\theta| - 4. \tag{85}$$

Analogously one obtains the estimate

$$|L_{n_i+1}[R;x]| > (p^2+4p)|\cos(n_i+1)\theta| - 4. \tag{86}$$

Since $\dfrac{\pi}{p} \leqq \theta \leqq \pi - \dfrac{\pi}{p}$ it follows that

$$\sin\theta \geqq \sin\frac{\pi}{p} \geqq \frac{2}{p}. \tag{87}$$

On the other hand

$$\sin\theta = \sin(n+1)\theta\cos n\theta - \sin n\theta\cos(n+1)\theta,$$

and hence

$$\sin\theta \leqq |\cos n_i\theta| + |\cos(n_i+1)\theta|.$$

For at least one of the two values $n = n_i$ and $n = n_i + 1$ (which we then simply denote by n) the inequality [12]

$$|\cos n\theta| \geqq \frac{1}{p}$$

must hold, so that according to (85) and (86) for just this value

$$|L_n[R; x]| > p. \tag{88}$$

The polynomial $R(x)$ therefore satisfies both conditions (81) and (82).

Remark. As we have seen, the index $n = n(x)$ for which (88) is satisfied can be taken from the finite sequence $n_1, n_1 + 1, n_2, \ldots, n_{m-1}, n_{m-1} + 1$; hence $n > p$. If we denote the number $n_{m-1} + 1$ by $N(p)$ (whereby it is important that m is completely determined by the given number p), then we have moreover that

$$n(x) \leqq N(p) \qquad \left(- \cos \frac{\pi}{p} \leqq x \leqq \cos \frac{\pi}{p}\right)$$

Theorem. *There exists a continuous function $f(x)$ on the interval $[-1, +1]$ for which the interpolation process with nodes*

$$x_k^{(n)} = \cos \frac{2k - 1}{2n} \pi \qquad (k = 1, 2, \ldots, n)$$

diverges at all points of the interval $(-1, +1)$.

Proof. The proof of this—as that of the FABER theorem—proceeds by the "sliding hump" method. We set

$$\lambda_n = \max \sum_{k=1}^{n} \left| \frac{T_n(x)}{T_n'(x_k^{(n)})(x - x_k^{(n)})} \right| \qquad (-1 \leqq x \leqq 1).$$

Then for every function $f(x)$ defined on $[-1, +1]$

$$|L_n[f; x]| \leqq \lambda_n \max |f(x)|.$$

After this remark we construct polynomials $R_p(x)$ for $p = 3, 4, 5, \ldots$ as called for in Lemma 4 and denote by $r(p)$ the degree of the polynomial $R_p(x)$ and by $n(x, p)$ the index n such that

$$|L_n[R_p; x]| > p \qquad \left(- \cos \frac{\pi}{p} \leqq x \leqq \cos \frac{\pi}{p}\right).$$

---

[12] Otherwise (87) would be impossible.

Then according to the remark preceding the theorem

$$p \leqq n(x, p) \leqq N(p) \qquad \left(- \cos \frac{\pi}{p} \leqq x \leqq \cos \frac{\pi}{p}\right). \tag{89}$$

We now choose a sequence $p_1, p_2, p_3, \ldots$ which satisfies the following conditions:

$$p_1 = 3,$$
$$p_{k+1} > \max \{r(p_1), r(p_2), \ldots, r(p_k)\}, \tag{90}$$

$$p_{k+1} > p_k^2 \tag{91}$$

$$p_{k+1} > \max \{\lambda_{pk}^2, \lambda_{pk+1}^2, \ldots, \lambda_{N(pk)}^2\}; \tag{92}$$

we assert that the function

$$f(x) = \sum_{k=1}^{\infty} \frac{R_{pk}(x)}{\sqrt{p_k}} \tag{93}$$

possesses the property asserted in the theorem.

First of all, the series (93) represents a continuous function, since it converges uniformly, being majorized by the series

$$\sum_{k=1}^{\infty} \frac{2}{\sqrt{p_k}} \tag{94}$$

which converges because of (91).

If now $-1 < x_0 < 1$ and m is so large that

$$- \cos \frac{\pi}{p_m} \leqq x_0 \leqq \cos \frac{\pi}{p_m},$$

then we have

$$f(x) = A(x) + \frac{R_{pm}(x)}{\sqrt{p_m}} + B(x),$$

where

$$A(x) = \sum_{k=1}^{m-1} \frac{R_{pk}(x)}{\sqrt{p_k}}, \qquad B(x) = \sum_{k=m+1}^{\infty} \frac{R_{pk}(x)}{\sqrt{p_k}}.$$

With $n = n(x_0, p_m)$ we obtain

$$L_n[f; x_0] = L_n[A; x_0] + \frac{1}{\sqrt{p_m}} L_n[R_{pm}; x_0] + L_n[B; x_0]. \tag{95}$$

The second term of the righthand side of this equation is greater in absolute value than $\sqrt{p_m}$. Further, the degree of $A(x)$ is at most equal to max $\{r(p_1),$ $r(p_2), \ldots, r(p_{m-1})\}$, and hence according to (89)

$$L_n[A; x] = A(x),$$

so that for all values x in $[-1, +1]$ the estimate

$$|L_n[A; x]| \leqq S \tag{96}$$

holds, where S denotes the sum of the series (94). Now finally we have for all x in $[-1, +1]$

$$|L_n[B; x]| \leqq \lambda_n \max |B(x)|,$$

whence

$$|L_n[B; x]| \leqq \lambda_n \sum_{k=m+1}^{\infty} \frac{2}{\sqrt{p_k}}.$$

But from (91)

$$p_{m+2} > p_{m+1}^2, \ p_{m+3} > p_{m+2}p_{m+1}, \ \cdots, \ p_{m+i+1} > p_{m+i}p_{m+1}, \ \cdots,$$

as is easily proved by induction on i. Therefore

$$\sum_{k=m+1}^{\infty} \frac{2}{\sqrt{p_k}} < \frac{1}{\sqrt{p_{m+1}}} \left[2 + \frac{2}{\sqrt{p_{m+1}}} + \frac{2}{\sqrt{p_{m+2}}} + \cdots \right] < \frac{2 + S}{\sqrt{p_{m+1}}},$$

whence it follows that

$$|L_n[B; x]| \leqq \frac{\lambda_n}{\sqrt{p_{m+1}}} (2 + S),$$

and therefore from (92)

$$|L_n[B; x]| \leqq 2 + S.$$

Together with (95) and (96) this gives

$$|L_n[f; x_0]| > \sqrt{p_m} - 2(1 + S).$$

Letting m tend to infinity, we obtain [13]

$$\lim L_n[f; x_0] = \infty. \tag{97}$$

wherewith the theorem is proved. It is possible without great difficulty to construct a function for which the interpolation process diverges not only in

[13] In relation (97) the index n does not range over the entire set of natural numbers, but only over the monotone subsequence $n = n(x_0, p_m)$.

the interval $(-1, +1)$, but on the closed interval $[-1, +1]$ as well: one need only add to $f(x)$ a continuous function $g(x)$ for which the interpolation process converges in the interval $(-1, +1)$ but diverges at the points ± 1; however, we shall not undertake the construction of such a function here.

In a similar way, it is possible to construct a continuous, 2π-periodic function for which the interpolation process with nodes

$$x_k^{(n)} = \frac{2k\pi}{2n+1} \qquad (k = 0, 1, 2, \ldots, 2n) \quad (98)$$

diverges at all points of the interval $[0, 2\pi]$. We have earlier indicated the analogy between interpolation polynomials for a function $f(x)$ with nodes (98) and the FOURIER partial sums for the function. Because of this analogy, before the work of GRUNWALD and MARCINKIEWICZ appeared many people were of the opinion that the problem of constructing a continuous, 2π-periodic function for which the interpolation process with nodes (98) diverged everywhere was, if not equivalent, at least closely related to the problem of finding a continuous, 2π-periodic function with everywhere divergent FOURIER series. However, this is not the case. As we have remarked in Volume I, the latter problem is still completely unsolved.[14]

[14] A. N. KOLMOGOROFF[1] has however demonstrated a summable function with everywhere divergent FOURIER series.

CHAPTER III

THE CONVERGENCE OF INTERPOLATION PROCESSES

§1. The Role of the Function $\lambda_n(x)$

We consider—as heretofore—a matrix of nodes in a finite interval $[a, b]$

$$\left.\begin{aligned}
&x_1^{(1)}, \\
&x_1^{(2)}, \quad x_2^{(2)}, \\
&\cdots\cdots\cdots\cdots\cdots \\
&x_1^{(n)}, \quad x_2^{(n)}, \quad \ldots, \quad x_n^{(n)}, \\
&\cdots\cdots\cdots\cdots\cdots
\end{aligned}\right\} \tag{99}$$

We define

$$\omega_n(x) = \prod_{k=1}^n (x - x_k^{(n)}), \qquad l_k^{(n)}(x) = \frac{\omega_n(x)}{\omega_n'(x_k^{(n)})(x - x_k^{(n)})},$$

$$\lambda_n(x) = \sum_{k=1}^n |l_k^{(n)}(x)|, \qquad \lambda_n = \max_{a \le x \le b} |\lambda_n(x)|.$$

As we already know, for any arbitrary matrix (99) the numbers λ_n tend to infinity. However, in general we can say that the class of functions for which the interpolation process converges is broader the slower the increase of the numbers λ_n. We prove

Theorem 1. *Let $f(x) \in C([a, b])$ and let E_n be its best approximation by polynomials of H_n. If*

$$\lim_{n \to \infty} \lambda_n(x_0)E_{n-1} = 0,$$

then the interpolation polynomial $L_n[f; x]$ which coincides with $f(x)$ at the nodes $x_k^{(n)}$ ($k = 1, 2, \ldots, n$) tends with increasing n at the point x_0 to the value $f(x_0)$. If

$$\lim_{n \to \infty} \lambda_n E_{n-1} = 0,$$

then [1] *$L_n[f; x]$ converges uniformly to $f(x)$ on $[a, b]$.*

---

[1] On the necessity of the condition stated in the theorem cf. S. M. Losinski [4].

Proof. Let $P_{n-1}(x)$ be the polynomial of H_{n-1} of least deviation from $f(x)$. Since $L_n[P_{n-1}; x] = P_{n-1}(x)$

$$|L_n[f; x] - f(x)| \leq |L_n[f; x] - L_n[P_{n-1}; x]| + |P_{n-1}(x) - f(x)|.$$

But now

$$L_n[f; x] - L_n[P_{n-1}; x] = L_n[f - P_{n-1}; x],$$

and moreover for every function $f(x)$ the estimate

$$|L_n[f; x]| \leq \lambda_n(x) \max |f(x)|;$$

is valid; therefore

$$|L_n[f; x] - f(x)| \leq [\lambda_n(x) + 1]E_{n-1};$$

the remainder of the proof is obvious.

Addendum. This theorem can clearly be sharpened as follows: *If S is a point set contained in $[a, b]$ and μ_n the upper bound of $\lambda_n(x)$ on this set, then the condition*

$$\lim_{n \to \infty} \mu_n E_{n-1} = 0$$

is sufficient for the uniform convergence of $L_n[f; x]$ to $f(x)$ on the set S.

An application of Theorem 1 is the following

Theorem 2 (S. N. BERNSTEIN [6]). *If the matrix* (99) *is composed of the* TCHEBYSHEFF *nodes*

$$x_k = x_k^{(n)} = \cos \frac{2k-1}{2n} \pi,$$

then

$$\lambda_n \leq 8 + \frac{4}{\pi} \ln n. \tag{100}$$

Proof. In this case

$$\lambda_n(x) = \frac{1}{n} \sum_{k=1}^{n} \left| \frac{T_n(x)}{x - x_k} \right| \sqrt{1 - x_k^2} \tag{101}$$

where $T_n(x) = \cos (n \arccos x)$. Setting

$$\theta = \arccos x, \qquad \theta_k = \theta_k^{(n)} = \frac{2k-1}{2n} \pi,$$

we have

$$\lambda_n(x) = \frac{1}{n} \sum_{k=1}^{n} \left| \frac{\cos n\theta}{\cos \theta - \cos \theta_k} \right| \sin \theta_k.$$

If θ coincides with one of the points θ_k, then $\lambda_n(x) = 1$, and there is nothing further to prove. Suppose then that

$$\theta_m < \theta < \theta_{m-1}.$$

Then

$$\lambda_n(x) = \frac{1}{n} \sum_{k=1}^{m} \frac{|\cos n\theta|}{\cos \theta_k - \cos \theta} \sin \theta_k + \frac{1}{n} \sum_{k=m+1}^{n} \frac{|\cos n\theta|}{\cos \theta - \cos \theta_k} \sin \theta_k, \quad (102)$$

where the first sum drops out if $0 \leqq \theta < \theta_1$ and the second drops out if $\theta_n < \theta \leqq \pi$. Both sums can be estimated in the same manner; we shall estimate the first one (whereby we naturally suppose that $\theta_1 < \theta$). Denoting this sum by σ, we have

$$\sigma = \frac{1}{n} \sum_{k=1}^{m-2} \frac{|\cos n\theta|}{\cos \theta_k - \cos \theta} \sin \theta_k + \frac{1}{n} \frac{|\cos n\theta|}{\cos \theta_{m-1} - \cos \theta} \sin \theta_{m-1}$$

$$+ \frac{1}{n} \frac{|\cos n\theta|}{\cos \theta_m - \cos \theta} \sin \theta_m. \quad (103)$$

In case $m = 1$ the sum σ possesses only the third summand, in case $m = 2$ only the second and third, and in case $m > 2$ all three.

According to Lemma 2 of Chapter II, § 3, the second and third summands do not exceed 2. Therefore

$$\sigma \leqq 4 + \frac{1}{n} \sum_{k=1}^{m-2} \frac{\sin \theta_k}{\cos \theta_k - \cos \theta}.$$

Now for $0 \leqq x < \theta$ the function

$$\frac{\sin x}{\cos x - \cos \theta}$$

is increasing. Hence

$$\frac{\sin \theta_k}{\cos \theta_k - \cos \theta} \leqq \frac{\sin x}{\cos x - \cos \theta} \qquad (\theta_k \leqq x \leqq \theta_{k+1}).$$

From this it follows that

$$\frac{\pi}{n} \frac{\sin \theta_k}{\cos \theta_k - \cos \theta} < \int_{\theta_k}^{\theta_{k+1}} \frac{\sin x \, dx}{\cos x - \cos \theta}$$

and hence

$$\frac{1}{n} \sum_{k=1}^{m-2} \frac{\sin \theta_k}{\cos \theta_k - \cos \theta} < \frac{1}{\pi} \int_{\theta_1}^{\theta_{m+1}} \frac{\sin x \, dx}{\cos x - \cos \theta}.$$

Therefore

$$\sigma < 4 + \frac{1}{\pi} \int\limits_{0}^{\theta_{m-1}} \frac{\sin x \, dx}{\cos x - \cos \theta} = 4 + \frac{1}{\pi} \ln \frac{1 - \cos \theta}{\cos \theta_{m-1} - \cos \theta}.$$

Since

$$1 - \cos \theta \leqq 2, \quad \cos \theta_{m-1} - \cos \theta > \cos \theta_{m-1} - \cos \theta_m,$$

it further follows that

$$\sigma < 4 - \frac{1}{\pi} \ln \sin \frac{\theta_{m-1} + \theta_m}{2} - \frac{1}{\pi} \ln \sin \frac{\pi}{2n}.$$

Now

$$\frac{\pi}{2n} < \theta_{m-1} < \pi - \frac{\pi}{2n}, \qquad \frac{\pi}{2n} < \theta_m \leqq \pi - \frac{\pi}{2n},$$

and hence

$$\sin \frac{\theta_{m-1} + \theta_m}{2} > \sin \frac{\pi}{2n}.$$

Therefore

$$\sigma < 4 - \frac{2}{\pi} \ln \sin \frac{\pi}{2n}$$

and $\left(\text{since } \sin \dfrac{2\pi}{n} > \dfrac{1}{n}\right)$ a fortiori

$$\sigma < 4 + \frac{2}{\pi} \ln n.$$

The same estimate is also obtained for the second sum in (102); the theorem is herewith proved.

Corollary.   *If a function $f(x)$ satisfies the* Dini-Lipschitz *condition*

$$\lim_{\delta \to 0} \omega(\delta) \ln \delta = 0, \tag{104}$$

on the interval $[-1, +1]$, then the interpolation polynomial $L_n[f; x]$ constructed with the Tchebysheff *nodes converges uniformly to $f(x)$ on $[-1, +1]$.*

Proof.   In this case

$$\lim_{n \to \infty} \omega\left(\frac{1}{n-1}\right) \ln n = 0$$

and according to the JACKSON theorem

$$E_{n-1} \leqq 12\omega \left(\frac{1}{n-1}\right).$$

Remark. There is a theorem analogous to Theorem 1 which holds for trigonometric interpolation; $f(x)$ is then understood to be a 2π-periodic function, and E_n is its best approximation by trigonometric polynomials. The function $\lambda_n(x)$ is then defined by the formula

$$\lambda_n(x) = \sum_{k=0}^{2n} |f_k^{(n)}(x)|,$$

where the basis polynomials $t_k^{(n)}(x)$ are given by equation (34). In the case of equally spaced nodes

$$x_k^{(n)} = \frac{2k\pi}{2n+1} \qquad (k = 0, 1, \ldots, 2n) \quad (105)$$

the estimate

$$\lambda_n(x) < A + B \ln n,$$

holds for the function $\lambda_n(x)$, which says essentially the same thing as equation (100). For 2π-periodic functions which satisfy condition (104), therefore, the interpolation process with nodes (105) converges uniformly on the entire axis.

§2. The Theorems of GRÜNWALD and TURÁN

G. GRUNWALD and P. TURAN in a joint study investigated matrices (99) consisting of roots of orthogonal polynomial systems and arrived at interesting results. We shall here present a portion of their discoveries.

Here $\{\omega_n(x)\}$ is understood to be an orthogonal system of polynomials on $[a, b]$ with weight $p(x)$, and

$$x_1^{(n)} < x_2^{(n)} < \cdots < x_n^{(n)} \tag{106}$$

are the roots of the polynomial $\omega_n(x)$. If $f(x)$ is any function defined on $[a, b]$, let $L_n[f; x]$ be its interpolation polynomial with nodes (106).

Lemma. *If $i \neq k$ the basis polynomials*

$$l_i^{(n)}(x) = \frac{\omega_n(x)}{\omega_n'(x_i^{(n)})(x - x_i^{(n)})}, \qquad l_k^{(n)}(x) = \frac{\omega_n(x)}{\omega_n'(x_k^{(n)})(x - x_k^{(n)})}$$

are orthogonal with weight $p(x)$ on $[a, b]$.

Proof.   The fraction

$$q(x) = \frac{\omega_n(x)}{(x - x_i^{(n)})(x - x_k^{(n)})}$$

is a polynomial of degree $n - 2$ and is hence orthogonal on $[a, b]$ (with weight $p(x)$) to the polynomial $\omega_n(x)$; since

$$l_i^{(n)}(x)l_k^{(n)}(x) = \frac{q(x)\omega_n(x)}{\omega_n'(x_i^{(n)})\omega_n'(x_k^{(n)})},$$

it follows that

$$\int_a^b p(x)l_i^{(n)}(x)l_k^{(n)}(x)\, dx = 0. \tag{107}$$

Corollary.   *With the same notation*

$$\sum_{k=1}^n \int_a^b p(x)[l_k^{(n)}(x)]^2\, dx = \int_a^b p(x)\, dx. \tag{108}$$

Proof.   It has been noted in Chapter I that

$$\sum_{k=1}^n l_k^{(n)}(x) = 1.$$

Squaring this equality, multiplying with the weight $p(x)$, and integrating, we obtain (108), since according to (107) the integral over all cross terms vanishes.

Theorem 1.   *Let $a = -1$, $b = +1$. If the weight function $p(x)$ satisfies the condition*

$$p(x) \geqq m > 0, \tag{109}$$

then

$$\lambda_n \leqq An \tag{110}$$

and for $-1 < x < +1$

$$\lambda_n(x) \leqq \frac{B\sqrt{n}}{\sqrt{1 - x^2}}. \tag{111}$$

Proof.   We choose an $x_0 \in [-1, +1]$ and put

$$\varepsilon_k = \text{sign } \{l_k^{(n)}(x_0)\};$$

we thereupon introduce the function

$$\psi(x) = \sum_{k=1}^{n} \varepsilon_k l_k^{(n)}(x)$$

This is a polynomial of degree $n - 1$, and hence

$$\psi(x) = \sum_{k=0}^{n-1} c_k \hat{X}_k(x),$$

where the functions $\hat{X}_k(x)$ are normalized LEGENDRE polynomials, and the coefficients c_k are the FOURIER coefficients of $\psi(x)$ in the system of LEGENDRE polynomials. Applying the CAUCHY inequality to the righthand side we obtain

$$\psi^2(x) \leqq \left[\sum_{k=0}^{n-1} c_k^2 \right] \left[\sum_{k=0}^{n-1} \hat{X}_k^2(x) \right]. \tag{112}$$

With the help of the PARSEVAL formula and inequality (109) we find

$$\sum_{k=0}^{n-1} c_k^2 = \int_{-1}^{+1} \psi^2(x)\, dx \leqq \frac{1}{m} \int_{-1}^{+1} p(x)\psi^2(x)\, dx.$$

But since the numbers ε_k can assume only the values $-1, 0, +1$, it follows from (107) and (108) that

$$\int_{-1}^{+1} p(x)\psi^2(x)\, dx = \int_{-1}^{+1} p(x) \left[\sum_{k=1}^{n-1} \varepsilon_k l_k^{(n)}(x) \right]^2 dx \leqq \int_{-1}^{+1} p(x)\, dx.$$

Hence

$$\sum_{k=0}^{n-1} c_k^2 \leqq M^2 = \frac{1}{m} \int_{-1}^{+1} p(x)\, dx. \tag{113}$$

On the other hand, in Chapter V of Volume II (see there formulas (128), (136), and (140)) we established the estimates

$$\left. \begin{array}{c} |\hat{X}_k(x)| \leqq \sqrt{\dfrac{2k + 1}{2}} \\[2mm] (-1 \leqq x \leqq 1, \quad k = 0, 1, 2, \ldots), \\[2mm] |\hat{X}_k(x)| \leqq \sqrt{\dfrac{(2k + 1)\pi}{4k(1 - x^2)}} \\[2mm] (-1 < x < 1, \quad k = 1, 2, 3, \ldots) \end{array} \right\}. \tag{114}$$

If we put

$$\frac{3\pi}{4} = C^2,$$

then the second of these inequalities can be replaced by

$$|\hat{X}_k(x)| \leqq \frac{C}{\sqrt{1-x^2}} \qquad (-1 < x < 1); \quad (115)$$

in this form it also holds for $k = 0$. From (114) it follows that for $-1 \leqq x \leqq +1$

$$\sum_{k=0}^{n-1} \hat{X}_k^2(x) \leqq \frac{n^2}{2};$$

this together with (112) and (113) provides the estimate

$$|\psi(x)| \leqq \frac{Mn}{\sqrt{2}}.$$

Since $\psi(x_0) = \lambda_n(x_0)$, inequality (110) is proved. Inequality (111) follows analogously from (112), (113), and (115).

The JACKSON theorems of Volume I and the results of § 1 together with this theorem then yield

Theorem 2. *Under the conditions of Theorem 1*

$$\lim_{n \to \infty} L_n[f; x] = f(x) \tag{116}$$

uniformly on $[-1, +1]$ for every function $f(x)$ possessing a continuous derivative $f'(x)$ on this interval. If $f(x) \, \epsilon \, \mathrm{Lip} \, \alpha$ where $\alpha > \frac{1}{2}$, then (116) holds at every point of the interval $(-1, +1)$, and convergence is uniform on every interval $[a, b] \subset (-1, +1)$.

The conditions of Theorems 1 and 2 are satisfied in particular by every JACOBI weight $p(x) = (1 - x)^\alpha(1 + x)^\beta$ with $\alpha \leqq 0$, $\beta \leqq 0$. In addition, we now present (without proof) a result obtained by G. SZEGO[2]: If $f(x)$ satisfies only the DINI-LIPSCHITZ condition, then the interpolation process with the roots of the JACOBI polynomials as nodes converges uniformly in every closed interval $[a, b] \subset (-1, +1)$ for arbitrary exponents α, β.

[2] SZEGO [1], p. 328.

Theorem 3. *Let $a = -1$, $b = +1$. If the weight function $p(x)$ satisfies the condition*

$$p(x) \geqq \frac{m}{\sqrt{1 - x^2}} > 0, \tag{117}$$

then

$$\lambda_n \leqq A\sqrt{n}.$$

The proof of this inequality goes just as the proof of Theorem 1, only instead of an expansion of $\psi(x)$ in terms of LEGENDRE polynomials one uses an expansion in terms of TCHEBYSHEFF polynomials, the uniform boundedness of which on $[-1, +1]$ is then utilized.

On the basis of Theorem 3 it is easily shown that *under condition (117) relation (116) holds uniformly for all functions $f(x) \in \text{Lip } \alpha$ on $[-1, +1]$ if* $\alpha > \frac{1}{2}$.

Finally, we note that (117) is satisfied by every JACOBI weight $(1 - x)^\alpha (1 + x)^\beta$ with $\alpha \leqq -\frac{1}{2}$, $\beta \leqq -\frac{1}{2}$. However, this is—as previously pointed out—of relatively little interest, since convergence of the interpolation process over the roots of JACOBI polynomials can be proved for a much wider class of functions.

§3. Convergence in Mean

The FABER theorem of the preceding chapter implies that there does not exist a matrix of nodes which yields a uniformly convergent interpolation process for every continuous function. With respect to convergence in mean, the situation is much more favorable. In the notation of the preceding section, for an arbitrary orthogonal polynomial system with weight $p(x)$ we have the

Theorem. *The equation*

$$\lim_{n \to \infty} \int_a^b p(x) \{L_n[f; x] - f(x)\}^2 \, dx = 0 \tag{118}$$

holds for every continuous function $f(x)$.[3]

---

[3] This theorem is contained in the much more general results of a paper by P. ERDOS and P. TURAN [1]. The proof given in the text comes from a paper by R. O. KUSMIN and I. P. NATANSON [1].

Proof. Let E_n be the best approximation to $f(x)$ by polynomials of H_n, and let $P(x)$ be the polynomial of best approximation itself. Then

$$|P_{n-1}(x) - f(x)| \leq E_{n-1}, \tag{119}$$

and hence

$$\int_a^b p(x)[P_{n-1}(x) - f(x)]^2 \, dx \leq E_{n-1}^2 \int_a^b p(x) \, dx. \tag{120}$$

Now $P_{n-1}(x) = L_n[P_{n-1}; x]$, and hence

$$L_n[f; x] - P_{n-1}(x) = \sum_{k=1}^n [f(x_k^{(n)}) - P_{n-1}(x_k^{(n)})] \, l_k^{(n)}(x).$$

From (107) it now follows that

$$\int_a^b p(x)\{L_n[f; x] - P_{n-1}(x)\}^2 \, dx$$

$$= \sum_{k=1}^n [f(x_k^{(n)}) - P_{n-1}(x_k^{(n)})]^2 \int_a^b p(x)[l_k^{(n)}(x)]^2 \, dx.$$

With the help of (119) and (108) the last inequality can be rearranged to give

$$\int_a^b p(x)\{L_n[f; x] - P_{n-1}(x)\}^2 \, dx \leq E_{n-1}^2 \int_a^b p(x) \, dx. \tag{121}$$

Since $(A + B)^2 \leq 2(A^2 + B^2)$, it follows from (120) and (121) that

$$\int_a^b p(x) \, \{L_n[f; x] - f(x)\}^2 \, dx \leq 4E_{n-1}^2 \int_a^b p(x) \, dx,$$

wherewith the theorem is proved.

Corollary. *If the weight function $p(x)$ satisfies the condition*

$$p(x) \geq m > 0,$$

then

$$\lim_{n \to \infty} \int_a^b \{L_n[f; x] - f(x)\}^2 \, dx = 0. \tag{122}$$

There hereby arises the interesting question if perhaps (122) is also correct without additional conditions on the weight function. E. FELDHEIM [1] proved that this was not the case and at the same time noted without proof that there exist continuous functions for which the relation (122) does not hold with the weight

$$p(x) = \sqrt{1 - x^2}.$$

Such an example may be found in the paper by R. O. KUZMIN and I. P. NATANSON [1].[4]

§4. The FEJÉR Interpolation Process

Until now we have been concerned with questions arising in the LAGRANGE interpolation process. In the HERMITE process, i.e. in interpolating with multiple nodes, L. FEJÉR obtained a number of positive results. We present the simplest of these results in this section

Theorem (L. FEJÉR [2]). *Let*

$$x_k = x_k^{(n)} = \cos \frac{2k - 1}{2n} \pi \qquad (k = 1, 2, \ldots, n)$$

be the TCHEBYSHEFF nodes and $f(x)$ be a function continuous on $[-1, +1]$. If H_{2n-1} is a polynomial of degree at most $2n - 1$ which satisfies the conditions

$$H_{2n-1}(x_k) = f(x_k), \quad H'_{2n-1}(x_k) = 0, \tag{123}$$

then

$$\lim_{n \to \infty} H_{2n-1}(x) = f(x) \tag{124}$$

uniformly on $[-1, +1]$

Proof. For the TCHEBYSHEFF nodes

$$\omega(x) = T_n(x) = \cos(n \text{ arc cos } x).$$

Since

$$T'_n(x) = n \frac{\sin(n \text{ arc cos } x)}{\sqrt{1 - x^2}},$$

$$T''_n(x) = n \frac{x \sin(n \text{ arc cos } x) - n\sqrt{1 - x^2} \cos(n \text{ arc cos } x)}{(1 - x^2)^{3/2}}$$

it follows that

[4] Relative to all the questions raised in this section see also S. M. LOSINSKI [1, 2].

$$\omega'(x_k) = \frac{(-1)^{k-1}n}{\sqrt{1 - x_k^2}}, \quad \omega''(x_k) = \frac{(-1)^{k-1}n}{(1 - x_k^2)^{3/2}} x_k,$$

$$l_k(x) = \frac{(-1)^{k-1}T_n(x)}{n(x - x_k)} \sqrt{1 - x_k^2}.$$

Therefore, the general formulas (31) and (30) assume the following forms for the TCHEBYSHEFF nodes:

$$\left. \begin{aligned} A_k^{(n)}(x) &= \left[\frac{T_n(x)}{n(x - x_k)} \right]^2 (1 - xx_k); \\ B_k^{(n)}(x) &= \left[\frac{T_n(x)}{n(x - x_k)} \right]^2 (1 - x_k^2)(x - x_k), \end{aligned} \right\} \tag{125}$$

$$H_{2n-1}(x) = \sum_{k=1}^{n} y_k A_k^{(n)}(x) + \sum_{k=1}^{n} y_k' B_k^{(n)}(x). \tag{126}$$

Now $-1 < x_k < +1$, whence clearly

$$A_k^{(n)}(x) \geqq 0 \qquad (-1 \leqq x \leqq +1), \tag{127}$$

an inequality which—as we shall see—plays an extremely important role.

If now $P(x)$ is a polynomial of degree at most $2n - 1$, then it is identical with its HERMITE interpolation polynomial over the nodes $x_k^{(n)}$; hence

$$P(x) = \sum_{k=1}^{n} P(x_k) A_k^{(n)}(x) + \sum_{k=1}^{n} P_k'(x_k) B_k^{(n)}(x). \tag{128}$$

In particular,

$$\sum_{k=1}^{n} A_k^{(n)}(x) = 1. \tag{129}$$

According to (126), a polynomial which satisfies conditions (123) has the form

$$H_{2n-1}(x) = \sum_{k=1}^{n} f(x_k) A_k^{(n)}(x). \tag{130}$$

From this together with (129) and (127) it follows that

$$|H_{2n-1}(x) - f(x)| \leqq \sum_{k=1}^{n} |f(x_k) - f(x)| A_k^{(n)}(x). \tag{131}$$

Now given $\varepsilon > 0$, we choose δ such that the inequality $|x'' - x'| < \delta$ implies

$$|f(x'') - f(x')| < \varepsilon.$$

We now fix an $x \in [-1, +1]$ and partition the sequence $1, 2, \ldots, n$ into two sets I and II, whereby we put those indices k for which $|x - x_k| < \delta$ in I and all the rest in II. From (127) and (129) it is then clear that

$$\sum_{k \in I} |f(x_k) - f(x)| A_k^{(n)}(x) \leqq \varepsilon \sum_{k=1}^{n} A_k^{(n)}(x) = \varepsilon. \tag{132}$$

For $k \in II$ we obtain from (125) the estimate

$$A_k^{(n)}(x) \leqq \frac{2}{n^2 \delta^2}, \tag{133}$$

since $0 < 1 - xx_k < 2$ and $|T_n(x)| \leqq 1$. Denoting by M the maximum value of $|f(x)|$, we obtain

$$\sum_{k \in II} |f(x_k) - f(x)| A_k^{(n)}(x) \leqq \frac{4M}{n\delta^2}, \tag{134}$$

since the number of summands in the last sum is not greater than n. From (131), (132), and (134) we obtain finally

$$|H_{2n-1}(x) - f(x)| \leqq \varepsilon + \frac{4M}{n\delta^2},$$

and hence for sufficiently large values of n

$$|H_{2n-1}(x) - f(x)| < 2\varepsilon,$$

wherewith the theorem is proved.

§5. Generalization of the Preceding Results

The theorem just presented was discovered by FEJÉR in the year 1916. In 1930 he returned to the same problem and obtained much more general results. In presenting these we retain the notation of the preceding section.

From (125) it follows that

$$B_k^{(n)}(x) = \frac{x - x_k}{1 - xx_k} (1 - x_k^2) A_k^{(n)}(x). \tag{135}$$

The fraction

$$\varphi(x) = \frac{x - x_k}{1 - xx_k},$$

the denominator of which is strictly positive in $[-1, +1]$, satisfies for $|x| \leqq 1$ the inequality $|\varphi(x)| \leqq 1$, for

$$\varphi'(x) = \frac{1 - x_k^2}{(1 - xx_k)^2} > 0;$$

hence $\varphi(x)$ is an increasing function, and moreover $\varphi(1) = 1$, $\varphi(-1) = -1$. It thus follows from (135) that

$$|B_k^{(n)}(x)| \leqq A_k^{(n)}(x) \qquad (-1 \leqq x \leqq +1)$$

and thus on the basis of (129) that

$$\sum_{k=1}^{n} |B_k^{(n)}(x)| \leqq 1 \qquad (-1 \leqq x \leqq +1). \quad (136)$$

From these remarks we obtain

Theorem 1 (L. FEJÉR [3]).   *If at the* TCHEBYSHEFF *nodes*

$$x_k = x_k^{(n)} = \cos \frac{2k-1}{2n}\pi$$

a polynomial $P(x)$ of degree at most $2n - 1$ satisfies the conditions

$$|P(x_k)| \leqq A, \quad |P'(x_k)| \leqq B, \qquad (137)$$

then for all $x \,\epsilon\, [-1, +1]$ the inequality

$$|P(x)| \leqq A + B \qquad (138)$$

holds.

For the proof it suffices to write $P(x)$ in the form (128), whereupon on the basis of (127), (129), and (136) the truth of the assertion is evident.

Inequality (138) is moreover exact, since equality holds (with $n = 1$) for every linear function $f(x)$.

In addition to (136), the inequality

$$\sum_{k=1}^{n} |B_k^{(n)}(x)| \leqq \frac{1}{n}\left(8 + \frac{4}{\pi}\ln n\right) \quad (-1 \leqq x \leqq 1) \quad (139)$$

holds, since from (125) and the inequality $|T_n(x)| \leqq 1$

$$|B_k^{(n)}(x)| \leqq \frac{1}{n^2}\left|\frac{T_n(x)}{x - x_k}\right|(1 - x_k^2).$$

Hence, from (100) and (101) we obtain the estimate

$$\sum_{k=1}^{n} \frac{|B_k^{(n)}(x)|}{\sqrt{1 - x_k^2}} \leqq \frac{1}{n}\left(8 + \frac{4}{\pi}\ln n\right), \qquad (140)$$

which is considerably stronger than (139).

From (139) we obtain

Theorem 2 (L. Fejér [3]). *If a polynomial of degree at most $2n - 1$ satisfies conditions (137), then for all $x \in [-1, +1]$ the inequality*

$$|P(x)| \leqq A + \frac{B}{n}\left(8 + \frac{4}{\pi}\ln n\right)$$

holds.

Moreover, because of the inequality (140) the inequality (141) follows from the conditions

$$|P(x_k)| \leqq A, \qquad |P'(x_k)| \leqq \frac{B}{\sqrt{1 - x_k^2}},$$

which are more general than (137).

Estimates (139) and (140) make possible the following stronger versions of the theorems of § 4:

Theorem 3 (L. Fejér [3]). *Let $f(x)$ be a continuous function on $[-1, +1]$. If*

$$x_k = x_k^{(n)} = \cos\frac{2k - 1}{2n}\pi$$

and if the polynomial $H_{2n-1}(x)$ satisfies the conditions

$$H_{2n-1}(x_k) = f(x_k), \quad |H'_{2n-1}(x_k)| < \frac{\varepsilon_n}{\sqrt{1 - x_k^2}}\frac{n}{\ln n}, \tag{142}$$

where $\lim_{n \to \infty} \varepsilon_n = 0$, *then*

$$\lim_{n \to \infty} H_{2n-1}(x) = f(x)$$

uniformly on $[-1, +1]$.

Proof. According to (128) we have

$$H_{2n-1}(x) = \sum_{k=1}^{n} f(x_k)A_k^{(n)}(x) + \sum_{k=1}^{n} H'_{2n-1}(x_k)B_k^{(n)}(x).$$

From the proof of the theorem in the preceding section, the first sum tends uniformly to $f(x)$ with increasing n; from the second condition (142) and inequality (140) the same is true of the second sum. The theorem is herewith proved.

§6. Normal Matrices

We return to the matrix (99), where it is always assumed that all nodes $x_k = x_k^{(n)}$ lie within a finite segment $[a, b]$. In the notation of §1 of this chapter the HERMITE interpolation formula assumes the form

$$H_{2n-1}(x) = \sum_{k=1}^{n} y_k A_k^{(n)}(x) + \sum_{k=1}^{n} y_k' B_k^{(n)}(x)$$

where

$$A_k^{(n)}(x) = \left[1 - \frac{\omega''(x_k)}{\omega'(x_k)}\, (x - x_k) \right] l_k^2(x),$$

$$B_k^{(n)}(x) = (x - x_k) l_k^2(x),$$

$$l_k(x) = l_k^{(n)}(x) = \frac{\omega(x)}{\omega'(x_k)(x - x_k)}, \quad \omega(x) = \omega_n(x) = \prod_{k=1}^{n} (x - x_k).$$

Let us now consider the linear functions

$$v_k(x) = v_k^{(n)}(x) = 1 - \frac{\omega''(x_k)}{\omega'(x_k)}\, (x - x_k), \tag{143}$$

which are contained in the factors $A_k^{(n)}(x)$.

Definition. If for all $x \,\epsilon\, [a, b]$ and all k and n $(n = 1, 2, 3, \ldots; k = 1, 2, \ldots, n)$ the inequality

$$v_k^{(n)}(x) \geqq 0$$

holds, then we call (99) a *normal matrix*. We call it a *strict normal matrix* (or a *ρ-normal matrix*) if under the same conditions

$$v_k^{(n)}(x) \geqq \rho > 0.$$

FEJÉR introduced this concept in his paper [4] and proved its decisive role in the entire theory of interpolation (not only in the HERMITE but also in the LAGRANGE theory).

We shall present several of the principal results obtained by FEJÉR with regard to normal matrices. Before so doing we prove the existence of such matrices by giving examples, which are also due to FEJÉR.

Example 1. *If the nodes $x_k = x_k^{(n)}$ are the roots of the JACOBI polynomial $J_n^{(\alpha,\beta)}(x)$ then the matrix (99) is normal for $\alpha \leqq 0$ and $\beta \leqq 0$, and for $\alpha < 0$, $\beta < 0$ it is even strict normal.*

The underlying interval is here $[-1, +1]$; we have therefore only to prove that $v_k(1)$ and $v_k(-1)$ are non-negative. From formula (175) of Volume II the JACOBI polynomial $\omega(x) = J_n^{(\alpha,\beta)}(x)$ satisfies the differential equation

$$(1 - x^2)\omega''(x) + [\beta - \alpha - (\alpha + \beta + 2)x]\omega'(x)$$
$$+ n(\alpha + \beta + n + 1)\omega(x) = 0.$$

Now x_k is a root of $\omega(x)$, and hence

$$\frac{\omega''(x_k)}{\omega'(x_k)} = \frac{(\alpha + \beta + 2)x_k - \beta + \alpha}{1 - x_k^2};$$

therefore

$$v_k(x) = 1 - \frac{(\alpha + \beta + 2)x_k - \beta + \alpha}{1 - x_k^2}(x - x_k).$$

From this it follows that

$$v_k(1) = -\alpha + (1 + \beta)\frac{1 - x_k}{1 + x_k},$$

and hence

$$v_k(1) > -\alpha,$$

since $-1 < x_k < +1$ and $\beta > -1$. Analogously one finds that

$$v_k(-1) > -\beta;$$

hence for $-1 \leqq x \leqq +1$

$$v_k(x) > \rho = \min\{-\alpha, -\beta\}.$$

Special case: The roots of the LEGENDRE polynomials form a normal matrix, and the roots of the TCHEBYSHEFF polynomials a $\frac{1}{2}$-normal matrix.

Example 2. *The matrix whose nth row consists of the roots of the polynomial*

$$\omega(x) = \omega_n(x) = \int_{-1}^{x} X_{n-1}(t)\, dt,$$

where $X_{n-1}(t)$ is a LEGENDRE polynomial is 1-normal in $[-1, +1]$.
We first note that $\omega_1(x) = x + 1$, and hence $x_1^{(1)} = -1$.

If now $n \geqq 2$ the polynomial $\omega_n(x)$ may be written in the form

$$\omega_n(x) = \frac{1}{n(n-1)} (x^2 - 1) X'_{n-1}(x), \qquad (144)$$

for $X_{n-1}(t)$ satisfies the differential equation

$$(1 - t^2) X''_{n-1}(t) - 2t X'_{n-1}(t) + n(n-1) X_{n-1}(t) = 0, \qquad (145)$$

which we rearrange to

$$\frac{d}{dt} [(1 - t^2) X'_{n-1}(t)] + n(n-1) X_{n-1}(t) = 0.$$

Integrating this equation over the interval $[-1, x]$, we obtain equation (144) from which is evident the existence of n distinct roots $x_k = x_k^{(n)}$ of the polynomial $\omega_n(x)$ where

$$x_1^{(n)} = -1, \quad x_n^{(n)} = +1,$$

$$-1 < x_k^{(n)} < +1 \qquad (k = 2, 3, \ldots, n - 1).$$

From the definition of $\omega(x)$ it follows that for $n \geqq 2$ [5]

$$\frac{\omega''(x_k)}{\omega'(x_k)} = \frac{X'_{n-1}(x_k)}{X_{n-1}(x_k)}.$$

If $1 < k < n$, then x_k is a root of $X'_{n-1}(t)$, and hence

$$v_k(x) = 1.$$

If however $k = 1$, then it is evident from (145) that

$$\frac{X'_{n-1}(-1)}{X_{n-1}(-1)} = - \frac{n(n-1)}{2},$$

and hence

$$v_1(x) = 1 + \frac{n(n-1)}{2} (x + 1) \geqq 1.$$

Analogously one obtains

$$v_n(x) = 1 - \frac{n(n-1)}{2} (x - 1) \geqq 1.$$

---

[5] The case $n = 1$ is disposed of once and for all by noting that for any arbitrary matrix $\omega''_1(x) = 0$ and $v_1^{(1)}(x) = 1$.

Lemma 1.   *Given a normal matrix in $[a, b]$ and $0 < h < \dfrac{b-a}{2}$, the estimate*

$$v_k(x) \geqq \frac{h}{b-a} \qquad\qquad (146)$$

is valid on the interval $[a + h,\, b - h]$.

Proof.   Recall that $v_k(x)$ is a linear function, and $v_k(x_k) = 1$. If $v_k(x)$ is constant, then the estimate (146) is trivial. If $v_k(x)$ is a decreasing function, then

$$v_k(x) \geqq v_k(b - h) \qquad\qquad (x \leqq b - h).$$

Now [6]

$$\frac{v_k(x_k) - v_k(b)}{x_k - b} = \frac{v_k(b - h) - v_k(b)}{-h}.$$

From this it follows that

$$v_k(b - h) = v_k(b) + \frac{h}{b - x_k}[1 - v_k(b)]$$

$$\geqq v_k(b) + \frac{h}{b - a}[1 - v_k(b)] \geqq \frac{h}{b - a}.$$

The verification of (146) in the case where $v_k(x)$ is an increasing function is analogous.

Lemma 2.   *Given a normal matrix, then for $a + h \leqq x \leqq b - h$ the estimate*

$$\lambda_n(x) \leqq \sqrt{\frac{b-a}{h}}\,\sqrt{n} \qquad\qquad (147)$$

holds.   If however the matrix is ρ-normal, then

$$\lambda_n \leqq \frac{1}{\sqrt{\rho}}\,\sqrt{n}. \qquad\qquad (148)$$

Proof.   Now

$$\sum_{k=1}^{n} A_k^{(n)}(x) = 1, \qquad\qquad (149)$$

or equivalently

$$\sum_{k=1}^{n} v_k(x)l_k^2(x) = 1.$$

[6] The difference quotients of a linear function are constant.

From this and Lemma 1 it follows that

$$\sum_{k=1}^{n} l_k^2(x) \leqq \frac{b-a}{h} \qquad (a+h \leqq x \leqq b-h). \quad (150)$$

But now from the CAUCHY inequality

$$\lambda_n(x) = \sum_{k=1}^{n} |l_k(x)| \leqq \sqrt{n} \sqrt{\sum_{k=1}^{n} l_k^2(x)},$$

wherewith (147) is proved; the proof of (148) is analogous. From this lemma there follows immediately the

Theorem 1. *If $f(x) \, \epsilon$ LIP α with $\alpha > \dfrac{1}{2}$, then in interpolating over the nodes of a normal matrix the LAGRANGE interpolation polynomial $L_n(x)$ converges everywhere in the interval (a, b) to $f(x)$, and convergence is uniform on every interval $[a + h, a - h]$. If the matrix is strict normal, then $L_n(x)$ converges uniformly to $f(x)$ on the entire interval $[a, b]$.*

If in particular the nodes are roots of JACOBI polynomials $J_n^{(\alpha,\beta)}(x)$ with $\alpha \leqq 0$, $\beta \leqq 0$, then one obtains the same type of results as in § 2.

In conclusion, we present another theorem from the theory of the HERMITE interpolation polynomials.

Theorem 2. *Let $f(x)$ be defined and have a continuous derivative $f'(x)$ on $[a, b]$. If the matrix of nodes $x_k = x_k^{(n)}$ is normal and $H_{2n-1}(x)$ is the HERMITE interpolation polynomial which satisfies the conditions*

$$H_{2n-1}(x_k) = f(x_k), \quad H'_{2n-1}(x_k) = f'(x_k),$$

then

$$\lim_{n \to \infty} H_{2n-1}(x) = f(x). \quad (151)$$

everywhere in (a, b) and uniformly on every interval $[a + h, b - h]$. If the matrix is strict normal, then (151) holds uniformly on $[a, b]$.

Proof. Let E_n' be the best approximation to $f'(x)$ by polynomials of degree at most n, and let $P_n'(x)$ be the polynomial of best approximation itself. Then

$$|P_n'(x) - f'(x)| \leqq E_n' \quad (152)$$

Putting

$$P_n(x) = f(a) + \int_a^x P_n'(t) \, dt,$$

then

$$|P_n(x) - f(x)| \leqq (b - a)E_n'. \quad (153)$$

The degree of the polynomial $P_{2n-2}(x)$ is then not greater than $2n - 1$; hence

$$P_{2n-1}(x) = \sum_{k=1}^{n} P_{2n-2}(x_k)A_k^{(n)}(x) + \sum_{k=1}^{n} P'_{2n-2}(x_k)B_k^{(n)}(x).$$

On the other hand

$$H_{2n-1}(x) = \sum_{k=1}^{n} f(x_k)A_k^{(n)}(x) + \sum_{k=1}^{n} f'(x_k)B_k^{(n)}(x).$$

Recalling that $A_k^{(n)}(x) \geqq 0$ (since the matrix is normal) and taking into account (149), then from (152) and (153) it is evident that

$$|H_{2n-1}(x) - P_{2n-2}(x)| \leqq E'_{2n-2}\left[b - a + \sum_{k=1}^{n} |B_k^{(n)}(x)| \right].$$

But now $B_k^{(n)}(x) = (x - x_k)l_k^2(x)$ and $|x - x_k| \leqq b - a$; hence from (150)

$$\sum_{k=1}^{n} |B_k^{(n)}(x)| \leqq (b - a) \sum_{k=1}^{n} l_k^2(x) \leqq \frac{(b - a)^2}{h}.$$

It follows that

$$|H_{2n-1}(x) - P_{2n-2}(x)| \leqq (b - a)\left(1 + \frac{b - a}{h}\right) E'_{2n-2},$$

and hence on the basis of (153) that

$$|H_{2n-1}(x) - f(x)| \leqq (b - a)\left(2 + \frac{b - a}{h}\right) E'_{2n-2},$$

wherewith the first assertion is proved. The proof of the second assertion is similar, since for a ρ-normal matrix

$$\sum_{k=1}^{n} |B_k^{(n)}(x)| \leqq \frac{b - a}{\rho}.$$

The reader will find further details on normal matrices in the papers by D. L. Berman [1] and G. Grünwald [2].

CHAPTER IV

SEVERAL CONVERGENCE PROCESSES
RELATED TO INTERPOLATION

§1. The First BERNSTEIN Procedure

As we have seen in Chapter II, interpolation polynomials do not constitute a means of uniformly approximating any arbitrary continuous function. In this respect they are similar to partial FOURIER sums. However, in the first volume of this book we were able by starting with partial FOURIER sums to arrive at trigonometric polynomials which provided quite a useful and satisfactory uniform approximation. Examples of this were the FEJÉR or the DE LA VALLÉE POUSSIN sums. It is then natural to ask if one might arrive at such convergence processes by starting with interpolation polynomials. This idea was fruitfully pursued by S. N. BERNSTEIN in various directions, and he thereby discovered a great number of such convergence processes.[1] It is especially simple to arrive at these processes by considering trigonometric interpolation polynomials with the equally spaced nodes

$$x_k = x_k^{(n)} = \frac{2k\pi}{2n+1} \quad (k = 0, 1, \ldots, 2n), \quad (154)$$

since (as previously noted) the behaviour of these polynomials is in many respects similar to that of the partial FOURIER sums.

In this section we consider a process due to S. N. BERNSTEIN which is analogous to the CESARO-FEJÉR procedure.

Let

$$T_n(x) = A^{(n)} + \sum_{m=1}^{n} (a_m^{(n)} \cos mx + b_m^{(n)} \sin mx)$$

be the trigonometric polynomial which coincides with a function $f(x)$ from $C_{2\pi}$ at the nodes (154). Then according to § 5, Chapter I

---

[1] See also I. P. NATANSON [6].

$$A^{(n)} = \frac{1}{2n+1} \sum_{k=0}^{2n} f(x_k),$$

$$a_m^{(n)} = \frac{2}{2n+1} \sum_{k=0}^{2n} f(x_k) \cos mx_k, \qquad (155)$$

$$b_m^{(n)} = \frac{2}{2n+1} \sum_{k=0}^{2n} f(x_k) \sin mx_k.$$

We set $T_{n,o}(x) = A^{(n)}$ and

$$T_{n,p}(x) = A^{(n)} + \sum_{m=1}^{p} (a_m^{(n)} \cos mx + b_m^{(n)} \sin mx) \quad (1 \leqq p \leqq n).$$

Substituting in this the expressions (155) for the coefficients, we obtain

$$T_{n,p}(x) = \frac{1}{2n+1} \left\{ \sum_{k=0}^{2n} f(x_k) + 2 \sum_{m=1}^{p} \left[\sum_{k=0}^{2n} f(x_k) \cos m(x - x_k) \right] \right\}.$$

From this it follows that

$$T_{n,p}(x) = \frac{1}{2n+1} \sum_{k=0}^{2n} f(x_k) \left[1 + 2 \sum_{m=1}^{p} \cos m(x - x_k) \right],$$

which with the help of formula (41) becomes

$$T_{n,p}(x) = \frac{1}{2n+1} \sum_{k=0}^{2n} f(x_k) \frac{\sin \frac{2p+1}{2}(x - x_k)}{\sin \frac{x - x_k}{2}}, \qquad (156)$$

a representation of $T_{n,p}(x)$ which is also valid for $p = 0$. If we now put

$$U_q^{(n)}(x) = \frac{T_{n,0}(x) + T_{n,1}(x) + \cdots + T_{n,q}(x)}{q + 1},$$

then we obtain by means of formula (156)

$$U_q^{(n)}(x) = \frac{1}{(2n+1)(q+1)} \sum_{k=0}^{2n} \frac{f(x_k)}{\sin \frac{x - x_k}{2}} \left[\sum_{p=0}^{q} \sin \frac{2p+1}{2}(x - x_k) \right].$$

From formula (194) of Volume I

$$\sum_{p=0}^{q} \sin \frac{2p+1}{2} \alpha = \frac{\sin^2 \frac{q+1}{2} \alpha}{\sin \frac{\alpha}{2}},$$

and hence

$$U_q^{(n)}(x) = \frac{1}{(2n+1)(q+1)} \sum_{k=0}^{2n} f(x_k) \left[\frac{\sin \dfrac{q+1}{2}(x - x_k)}{\sin \dfrac{x - x_k}{2}} \right]^2. \qquad (157)$$

Theorem (S. N. BERNSTEIN [9]). *As n and q (with q ≦ n) increase without bound,*

$$\lim U_q^{(n)}(x) = f(x)$$

uniformly on the entire axis.

Proof.   Let us first consider the form assumed by $U_q^{(n)}(x)$ for $f(x) = 1$. In this case from (157)

$$U_q^{(n)}(x) = \frac{1}{(2n+1)(q+1)} \sum_{k=0}^{2n} \left[\frac{\sin \dfrac{q+1}{2}(x - x_k)}{\sin \dfrac{x - x_k}{2}} \right]^2. \qquad 158)$$

Also, if $f(x) \equiv 1$ then

$$A^{(n)} = 1,$$

$$a_m^{(n)} = \frac{2}{2n+1} \sum_{k=0}^{2n} \cos mx_k, \quad b_m^{(n)} = \frac{2}{2n+1} \sum_{k=0}^{2n} \sin mx_k.$$

We now show that for $1 \leq m \leq n$ the identity

$$\sum_{k=0}^{2n} \cos mx_k = \sum_{k=0}^{2n} \sin mx_k = 0 \qquad (159)$$

holds.   Both sums are the real or imaginary parts of the sum

$$\sum_{k=0}^{2n} e^{imx_k}.$$

Since however the nodes x_k form an arithmetic sequence

$$\sum_{k=0}^{2n} e^{imx_k} = \frac{1 - e^{i2m\pi}}{1 - e^{i\frac{2m\pi}{2n+1}}} = 0,$$

whence (159) follows.
  Hence $a_m^{(n)} = b_m^{(n)} = 0$, and

$$T_{n,p}(x) = A^{(n)} = 1 \qquad (p = 0, 1, \ldots, n)$$

for $f(x) \equiv 1$ therefore

$$U_q^{(n)}(x) = 1.$$

This together with (158) yields the identity

$$1 = \frac{1}{(2n+1)(q+1)} \sum_{k=0}^{2n} \left[\frac{\sin \dfrac{q+1}{2}(x-x_k)}{\sin \dfrac{x-x_k}{2}} \right]^2 . \tag{160}$$

From (157) and (160) it follows that

$$|U_q^{(n)}(x) - f(x)|$$

$$\leqq \frac{1}{(2n+1)(q+1)} \sum_{k=0}^{2n} |f(x_k) - f(x)| \left[\frac{\sin \dfrac{q+1}{2}(x-x_k)}{\sin \dfrac{x-x_k}{2}} \right]^2$$

Now given $\varepsilon > 0$ we choose a $\delta > 0$ such that $|x'' - x'| < \delta$ implies $|f(x'') - f(x')| < \varepsilon$. We now fix x and partition the sequence $0, 1, 2, \ldots, n$ into two sets I and II. k belongs to I if one of the following three cases occurs:

$$|x_k - x| < \delta, \quad |x_k - x + 2\pi| < \delta, \quad |x_k - x - 2\pi| < \delta;$$

k belongs to II if none of the three conditions is satisfied by x_k.

Since $f(x \pm 2\pi) = f(x)$, we obtain on the basis of (160) the estimate

$$\frac{1}{(2n+1)(q+1)} \sum_{k\in I} |f(x_k) - f(x)| \left[\frac{\sin \dfrac{q+1}{2}(x-x_k)}{\sin \dfrac{x-x_k}{2}} \right]^2 < \varepsilon .$$

Now for $k \in II$ [2]

$$\left| \sin \frac{x-x_k}{2} \right| \geqq \sin \frac{\delta}{2}.$$

Denoting by M the maximum value of $f(x)$, we obtain

$$\frac{1}{(2n+1)(q+1)} \sum_{k\in II} |f(x_k) - f(x)| \left[\frac{\sin \dfrac{q+1}{2}(x-x_k)}{\sin \dfrac{x-x_k}{2}} \right]^2$$

$$\leqq \frac{2M}{(2n+1)(q+1)\sin^2 \dfrac{\delta}{2}} \sum_{k=0}^{2n} \sin^2 \frac{q+1}{2}(x-x_k),$$

[2] Since clearly $|x_k - x| < 2\pi$, for $k \in II$:
$$\frac{\delta}{2} \leqq \left| \frac{x_k - x}{2} \right| \leqq \pi - \frac{\delta}{2} .$$

and hence

$$\frac{1}{(2n + 1)(q + 1)} \sum_{k \in \text{II}} | f(x_k) - f(x)| \left[\frac{\sin \dfrac{q + 1}{2} (x - x_k)}{\sin \dfrac{x - x_k}{2}} \right]^2 \leqq \frac{2M}{(q + 1) \sin^2 \dfrac{\delta}{2}} .$$

Therefore, for an arbitrary pair of values n and q (with $q \leqq n$)

$$| U_q^{(n)}(x) - f(x)| < \varepsilon + \frac{2M}{(q + 1) \sin^2 \dfrac{\delta}{2}} ,$$

wherewith the theorem is proved.

§2. The Second BERNSTEIN Procedure

A second method of constructing sums which converge uniformly to a function of $C_{2\pi}$ is an analogue of the ROGOSINSKI-BERNSTEIN procedure described in Chapter X, Volume I.

As above, let $T_n(x) \in H_n^T$ be the trigonometric polynomial which coincides with $f(x) \in C_{2\pi}$ at the nodes (154). Following S. N. BERNSTEIN,[3] we then put

$$U_n(x) = U_n[f; x] = \frac{T_n \left(x + \dfrac{\pi}{2n + 1} \right) + T_n \left(x - \dfrac{\pi}{2n + 1} \right)}{2} . \quad (161)$$

Theorem 1 (S. N. BERNSTEIN).   *For every function $f(x) \in C_{2\pi}$*

$$\lim_{n \to \infty} U_n(x) = f(x) \quad (162)$$

uniformly on the entire axis.

Proof.   In order to prove this theorem, we first establish several other propositions.

Theorem 2 (A. ZYGMUND).   *If $K(x)$ is a trigonometric polynomial of at most nth order, then* [4]

$$\int_0^{2\pi} | K'(x)| \, dx \leqq 2n \int_0^{2\pi} | K(x) \, dx . \quad (163)$$

---

[3] S. N. BERNSTEIN [9].   See also F. I. KHARSHILADZE [2] whose development we follow here.
[4] ZYGMUND [1], pp. 156–157.   In another work ZYGMUND proved that the factor 2 on the righthand side of inequality (163) could be dropped.

Proof. If

$$K(x) = A + \sum_{k=1}^{n} (a_k \cos kx + b_k \sin kx),$$

then

$$a_k = \frac{1}{\pi} \int_0^{2\pi} K(t) \cos kt \, dt,$$

$$b_k = \frac{1}{\pi} \int_0^{2\pi} K(t) \sin kt \, dt.$$

Substituting these expressions in the equation

$$K'(x) = \sum_{k=1}^{n} k(b_k \cos kx - a_k \sin kx),$$

we obtain

$$K'(x) = \frac{1}{\pi} \int_0^{2\pi} K(t) \left[\sum_{k=1}^{n} k \sin k(t - x) \right] dt.$$

But now

$$\int_0^{2\pi} K(t) \left[\sum_{k=1}^{n-1} k \sin (2n - k)(t - x) \right] dt = 0,$$

since the function

$$\sin (2n - k)(t - x) = \sin (2n - k)t \cos (2n - k)x$$
$$- \cos (2n - k)t \sin (2n - k)x$$

for $1 \leq k \leq n - 1$ in $[0, 2\pi]$ is orthogonal to the polynomial $K(x)$ the order of which is at most n. Hence

$$K'(x) = \frac{1}{\pi} \int_0^{2\pi} K(t) \left\{ n \sin n(t - x) \right.$$
$$\left. + \sum_{k=1}^{n-1} k[\sin k(t - x) + \sin (2n - k)(t - x)] \right\} dt,$$

whence it follows that

$$K'(x) = \frac{1}{\pi} \int_0^{2\pi} K(t) \sin n(t - x) \left[n + 2 \sum_{k=1}^{n-1} k \cos (n - k)(t - x) \right] dt.$$

From formula (89) of Volume I

$$n + 2 \sum_{k=1}^{n-1} k \cos (n - k)t \geqq 0,$$

and hence

$$|K'(x)| \leqq \frac{1}{\pi} \int_0^{2\pi} |K(t)| \left[n + 2 \sum_{k=1}^{n-1} k \cos (n - k)(t - x) \right] dt.$$

If we now integrate this inequality, whereby we interchange the order of integration on the righthand side and take into account the fact that

$$\int_0^{2\pi} \left[n + 2 \sum_{k=1}^{n-1} \cos (n - k)(t - x) \right] dx = 2n\pi,$$

we then arrive at (163).

Corollary.   *If $K(x) \epsilon H_n^T$ and $x_k = \dfrac{2k\pi}{2n + 1}$, then*

$$\left| \frac{1}{2n + 1} \sum_{k=0}^{2n} |K(x_k)| - \frac{1}{2\pi} \int_0^{2\pi} |K(t)| \, dt \right| \leqq \int_0^{2\pi} |K(t)| \, dt. \qquad (164)$$

Proof.   We have

$$\frac{1}{2\pi} \int_0^{2\pi} |K(t)| \, dt = \frac{1}{2\pi} \sum_{k=0}^{2n} \int_{x_k}^{x_{k+1}} |K(t)| \, dt.$$

Applying the mean value theorem to each summand, we find that

$$\frac{1}{2\pi} \int_0^{2\pi} |K(t)| \, dt = \frac{1}{2n + 1} \sum_{k=0}^{2n} |K(\xi_k)| \qquad (x_k \leqq \xi_k \leqq x_{k+1}).$$

The lefthand side of inequality (164) is therefore no greater than [5]

$$\frac{1}{2n + 1} \sum_{k=0}^{2n} |K(x_k) - K(\xi_k)| \leqq \frac{1}{2n + 1} \sum_{k=0}^{2n} \int_{x_k}^{\xi_k} |K'(t)| \, dt.$$

But now the intervals $[x_k, \xi_k]$ have no common interior point, and moreover they all lie in $[0, 2\pi]$.   Therefore,

[5] We recall that $||a| - |b|| \leqq |a - b|$.

$$\sum_{k=0}^{2n} \int_{x_k}^{\xi k} |K'(t)| \, dt \leqq \int_0^{2\pi} |K'(t)| \, dt;$$

this and (163) give (164).

We now return to the BERNSTEIN theorem. From (42) we obtain

$$T_n(x) = \frac{1}{2n+1} \sum_{k=0}^{2n} f(x_k) \frac{\sin \dfrac{2n+1}{2}(x_k - x)}{\sin \dfrac{x_k - x}{2}},$$

and hence

$$U_n(x) = \frac{1}{4n+2} \sum_{k=0}^{2n} f(x_k) \cos \frac{2n+1}{2}(x_k - x)$$

$$\times \left[\frac{1}{\sin\left(\dfrac{x_k - x}{2} + \dfrac{\pi}{4\pi + 2}\right)} - \frac{1}{\sin\left(\dfrac{x_k - x}{2} - \dfrac{\pi}{4n + 2}\right)} \right]. \tag{165}$$

For fixed x we now put

$$K(t) = \cos \frac{2n+1}{2}(t - x)$$

$$\times \left[\frac{1}{\sin\left(\dfrac{t - x}{2} + \dfrac{\pi}{4n + 2}\right)} - \frac{1}{\sin\left(\dfrac{t - x}{2} - \dfrac{\pi}{4n + 2}\right)} \right].$$

This is a trigonometric polynomial of nth order for which according to inequality (296) of Volume I the inequality

$$\int_0^{2\pi} |K(t)| \, dt < 8\pi^2$$

holds. Taking into account (164), we obtain

$$\frac{1}{4n+2} \sum_{k=0}^{2n} |K(x_k)| \leqq 2\pi + 4\pi^2.$$

From this and (165) it follows that

$$|U_n[f; x]| \leqq (2\pi + 4\pi^2) M, \tag{166}$$

where $M = \max |f(x)|$.

The rest is now easy. We denote by $T(x)$ the trigonometric polynomial of at most nth order which is of smallest deviation from $f(x)$ such that

$$|\, T(x) - f(x)\,| \leqq E_n,$$

and hence

$$|\, U_n[T - f; x]\,| \leqq (2\pi + 4\pi^2)E_n$$

or equivalently

$$|\, U_n[T; x] - U_n[f; x]\,| \leqq (2\pi + 4\pi^2)E_n.$$

Since now the polynomial $T(x)$ is identical with its interpolation polynomial,

$$U_n[T; x] = \frac{T\left(x + \dfrac{\pi}{2n+1}\right) + T\left(x - \dfrac{\pi}{2n+1}\right)}{2}.$$

This quantity differs from

$$\frac{f\left(x + \dfrac{\pi}{2n+1}\right) + f\left(x - \dfrac{\pi}{2n+1}\right)}{2} \tag{167}$$

by less than E_n, and the fraction (167) differs from $f(x)$ by less than $\omega\left(\dfrac{\pi}{2n+1}\right)$, where $\omega(\delta)$ is the modulus of continuity of $f(x)$. Therefore

$$|\, U_n[f; x] - f(x)\,| < (1 + 2\pi + 4\pi^2)E_n + \omega\left(\frac{2\pi}{2n+1}\right),$$

wherewith the theorem is proved.

§3. A Theorem of S. M. Losinski and the Procedure of S. J. Rappoport

The considerations of the preceding section allow considerable generalization.

Theorem 1 (S. M. Losinski). *Let*

$$\rho_0^{(0)},$$
$$\rho_0^{(1)}, \quad \rho_1^{(1)},$$
$$\cdots \cdots \cdots \cdots$$
$$\rho_0^{(n)}, \quad \rho_1^{(n)}, \quad \ldots, \quad \rho_n^{(n)},$$
$$\cdots \cdots \cdots \cdots$$

be a matrix of numbers which satisfy the conditions

$$\lim_{n \to \infty} \rho_k^{(n)} = 1,$$

$$\frac{1}{2\pi} \int_{-\pi}^{\pi} \left| \rho_0^{(n)} + 2 \sum_{k=1}^{n} \rho_k^{(n)} \cos kt \right| dt < K.$$

If then $f(x) \in C_{2\pi}$ and

$$T_n(x) = A^{(n)} + \sum_{m=1}^{n} (a_m^{(n)} \cos mx + b_m^{(n)} \sin mx)$$

is the polynomial which coincides with $f(x)$ at the nodes $x_k = \dfrac{2k}{2n+1}$ ($k = 0, 1,$

2, ..., 2n), then the polynomial

$$L_n(x) = L_n[f; x] = \rho_0^{(n)} A^{(n)} + \sum_{m=1}^{n} \rho_m^{(n)} (a_m^{(n)} \cos mx + b_m^{(n)} \sin mx)$$

converges uniformly to $f(x)$ with increasing n.[6]

Proof. We substitute the expressions (155) for the coefficients $A^{(n)}$, $a_m^{(n)}$, $b_m^{(n)}$ into $L_n(x)$. This gives

$$L_n(x) = \frac{1}{2n+1} \sum_{k=0}^{2n} f(x_k) \left[\rho_0^{(n)} + 2 \sum_{m=1}^{n} \rho_m^{(n)} \cos m(x_k - x) \right]$$

or

$$L_n(x) = \frac{1}{2n+1} \sum_{k=0}^{2n} f(x_k) K(x_k),$$

where for brevity we have put

$$K(t) = \rho_0^{(n)} + 2 \sum_{m=1}^{n} \rho_m^{(n)} \cos m(t - x).$$

By hypothesis

$$\frac{1}{2\pi} \int_{0}^{2\pi} |K(t)| \, dt < K.$$

Therefore from (164)

$$\frac{1}{2n+1} \sum_{k=0}^{2n} |K(x_k)| < (2\pi + 1)K,$$

and hence

$$|L_n[f; x]| \leqq (2\pi + 1)KM, \tag{168}$$

where $M = \max |f(x)|$.

[6] S. M. LOSINSKI [3], p. 237. The result obtained by LOSINSKI is somewhat more general than that given in the text.

Now let $\varepsilon > 0$ and

$$U(x) = R + \sum_{m=1}^{q} (r_m \cos mx + s_m \sin mx)$$

be a trigonometric polynomial such that

$$|U(x) - f(x)| < \varepsilon.$$

According to (168)

$$|L_n[U; x] - L_n[f; x]| < (2\pi + 1)K\varepsilon.$$

For $n \geqq q$ however the polynomial $U(x)$ is identical with its interpolation polynomial over the nodes x_k. Hence

$$L_n[U; x] = \rho_0^{(n)}R + \sum_{m=1}^{q} \rho_m^{(n)}(r_m \cos mx + s_m \sin mx).$$

From the hypothesis

$$\lim_{n \to \infty} \rho_m^{(n)} = 1$$

it follows that for sufficiently large n

$$|L_n[U; x] - U(x)| < \varepsilon.$$

For such values of n clearly

$$|L_n[f; x] - f(x)| < [(2\pi + 1)K + 2]\varepsilon,$$

wherewith the proof is completed.

The principal implication of this interesting theorem is that any procedure which starting with FOURIER partial sums yields a uniform approximation can be applied to trigonometric interpolation polynomials over equally spaced nodes with the same result.

If in particular we put

$$\rho_m^{(n)} = \frac{(n!)^2}{(n - m)!(n + m)!},$$

then the polynomial $L_n(x)$ becomes

$$R_n(x) = A^{(n)} + \sum_{m=1}^{n} \frac{(n!)^2}{(n - m)!(n + m)!}(a_m^{(n)} \cos mx + b_m^{(n)} \sin mx)$$

which with the help of (155) can be rearranged to

$$R_n(x) = \frac{1}{2n + 1} \sum_{k=0}^{2n} f(x_k)\left[1 + 2\sum_{m=1}^{n} \frac{(n!)^2}{(n - m)!(n + m)!} \cos m(x_k - x)\right].$$

According to formula (309) of Volume I

$$1 + 2 \sum_{m=1}^{n} \frac{(n!)^2}{(n-m)!(n+m)!} \cos mt = \frac{(2n)!!}{(2n-1)!!} \cos^{2n} \frac{t}{2},$$

wherewith $R_n(x)$ becomes

$$R_n(x) = \frac{(2n)!!}{(2n+1)!!} \sum_{k=0}^{2n} f(x_k) \cos^{2n} \frac{x_k - x}{2},$$

which is analogous to the integral of DE LA VALLÉE POUSSIN.   We therefore have [7]

Theorem 2 (S. J. RAPPOPORT).   *If $f(x) \, \epsilon \, C_{2\pi}$, then*

$$\lim_{n \to \infty} R_n(x) = f(x)$$

uniformly on the entire axis.

§4. The Third BERNSTEIN Procedure

In the preceding chapter we considered the FEJÉR interpolation procedure which consists in the construction of a polynomial $H_{2n-1}(x)$ which coincides with a given continuous function $f(x)$ at the TCHEBYSHEFF nodes $x_k^{(n)}$ and which converges uniformly to $f(x)$ with increasing n.   The polynomial $H_{2n-1}(x)$ is hereby a HERMITE interpolation polynomial rather than a LAGRANGE polynomial; it therefore has degree $2n - 1$ and coincides with $f(x)$ at only n nodes.   It is natural to look for a uniformly converging interpolation procedure in which the degree of the nth polynomial and the number of nodes form a ratio which is as close as possible to one. This problem was posed by S. N. BERNSTEIN [8] to whom is also due one of the possible solutions which we shall present in this section.

Let $x_k = x_k^{(n)} = \cos \theta_k$ where $\theta_k = \theta_k^{(n)} = \dfrac{2k-1}{2n} \pi$ be the system of TCHEBY-

SHEFF nodes.   Let l be a natural number which satisfies the condition $n \geqq 2l$ and partition the set of nodes

$$x_1^{(n)}, \; x_2^{(n)}, \; x_3^{(n)}, \; \ldots, \; x_n^{(n)}$$

[7] S. J. RAPPOPORT [1].   In this paper it is shown moreover that

$$\left| R_n(x) - f(x) \right| \leqq \omega \left(\frac{1}{\sqrt{n}} \right) \left(3 + \frac{2\pi}{\sqrt{2n+1}} \right)$$

where $\omega(\delta)$ is the modulus of continuity of $f(x)$.

[8] S. N. BERNSTEIN [8].

into subsets of $2l$ nodes each (if $2l$ does not divide n the last subset contains less than $2l$ nodes).

If $n = 2lq + r$ $(0 \leqq r < 2l)$ we obtain the subsets

$$
\begin{array}{cccc}
x_1, & x_2, & \ldots, & x_{2l}, \\
x_{2l+1}, & x_{2l+2}, & \ldots, & x_{4l}, \\
\cdot\,\cdot\,\cdot\,\cdot\,\cdot\,\cdot\,\cdot & \cdot\,\cdot\,\cdot\,\cdot\,\cdot\,\cdot\,\cdot & & \cdot\,\cdot\,\cdot\,\cdot\,\cdot \\
x_{2l(s-1)+1}, & x_{2l(s-1)+2}, & \ldots, & x_{2ls}, \\
\cdot\,\cdot\,\cdot\,\cdot\,\cdot\,\cdot\,\cdot\,\cdot & \cdot\,\cdot\,\cdot\,\cdot\,\cdot\,\cdot\,\cdot\,\cdot & & \cdot\,\cdot\,\cdot\,\cdot\,\cdot \\
x_{2lq+1}, & x_{2lq+2}, & \ldots, & x_{2lq+r}.
\end{array}
$$

Now let $f(x)$ be a continuous function on $[-1, +1]$. We set

$$
A_k = A_k^{(n)} = f(x_k^{(n)})
$$

for those k (of the sequence $1, 2, \ldots, n$) which are not divisible by $2l$; if however $2l$ divides k, $k = 2ls$ $(s = 1, 2, \ldots, q)$, then we set [9]
Using the numbers $A_k^{(n)}$ we construct the polynomial

$$
P_n(x) = P_n[f; x] = \sum_{k=1}^{n} A_k^{(n)} \frac{T_n(x)}{T_n'(x_k)(x - x_k)},
$$

where $T_n(x) = \cos (n \operatorname{arc} \cos x)$ is the TCHEBYSHEFF polynomial. The degree of the polynomial $P_n(x)$ is $n - 1$. Since $P_n(x_k^{(n)}) = A_k^{(n)}$ for all k which are not multiples of $2l$,

$$
P_n(x_k^{(n)}) = f(x_k^{(n)}).
$$

Hence, $P_n(x)$ coincides with $f(x)$ at the $n - q$ nodes $x_k^{(n)}$ for which $k \neq 2l$, $4l, \ldots, 2lq$. The relation of the degree of this polynomial to the number of nodes is therefore expressed by the fraction

$$
\frac{n-1}{n-q}.
$$

But now $q = \dfrac{n-r}{2l}$; hence

$$
\lim_{n \to \infty} \frac{n-1}{n-q} = \frac{2l}{2l-1},
$$

[9] If $l = 4$ for example

$$
A_{16} = [f(x_9) + f(x_{11}) + f(x_{13}) + f(x_{15})] - [f(x_{10} + f(x_{12}) + f(x_{14})].
$$

$$
A_{2ls} = A_{2ls}^{(n)} = [f(x_{2l(s-1+)1}) + f(x_{2l(s-1)+3}) + \cdots + f(x_{2ls-1})]
$$
$$
- [f(x_{2l(s-1)+2}) + f(x_{2l(s-1)+4}) + \cdots + f(x_{2ls-2})].
$$

and this quantity is arbitrarily close to one for sufficiently large l (it is to be noted that l is a selected fixed number).

We now prove that

$$\lim_{n \to \infty} P_n(x) = f(x) \qquad (169)$$

uniformly on $[-1, +1]$.

To this end we first note that

$$\sum_{k=1}^{n} \frac{T_n(x)}{T'_n(x_k)(x - x_k)} = 1,$$

and hence

$$P_n(x) - f(x) = \sum_{k=1}^{n} [A_k - f(x)] \frac{T_n(x)}{T'_n(x_k)(x - x_k)}.$$

If we here substitute the well-known expressions for $T(x)$ and $T'(x)$ we obtain

$$P_n(x) - f(x) = \frac{\cos(n \arccos x)}{n} \sum_{k=1}^{n} (-1)^{k+1}[A_k - f(x)] \frac{\sqrt{1 - x_k^2}}{x - x_k}$$

or, with $\theta = \arccos x$,

$$P_n(x) - f(x) = \frac{1}{n} \sum_{k=1}^{n} (-1)^{k+1}[A_k - f(x)] \frac{\cos n\theta}{\cos \theta - \cos \theta_k} \sin \theta_k.$$

Now let $\theta_\rho \leqq \theta < \theta_{\rho+1}$. We decompose the last sum according to the scheme

$$P_n(x) - f(x) = \sum_{k=1}^{p} + \sum_{k=p+1}^{n}$$

into two sums (for $\theta < \theta_1$ the first sum drops out, and for $\theta \geqq \theta_n$ the second sum drops out). Since both sums can be handled in the same manner, we consider only the second

$$\tau_n(x) = \frac{1}{n} \sum_{k=p+1}^{n} (-1)^{k+1}[A_k - f(x)] \frac{\cos n\theta}{\cos \theta - \cos \theta_k} \sin \theta_k.$$

We hereby assume that $\theta < \theta_n$. With increasing n the number of nodes θ_k which lie in the interval (θ, π) also increases without bound. Now let h be any natural number that is greater than $2l$ (we shall specify it more precisely later), and let n be so large that $n - p$ (the number of nodes $\theta = \theta_k^{(n)}$ in (θ, π)) is greater than h; we then put

$$\tau'_n(x) = \frac{1}{n} \sum_{k=p+1}^{p+h} (-1)^{k+1}[A_k - f(x)] \frac{\cos n\theta}{\cos \theta - \cos \theta_k} \sin \theta_k$$

and

$$\tau''_n(x) = \tau_n(x) - \tau'_n(x).$$

If now k is one of the numbers $p + 1, p + 2, \ldots, p + h$ which is not divisible by $2l$, then

$$|A_k - f(x)| = |f(x_k) - f(x)| \leqq \omega(|x_k - x|) \leqq \omega(\theta_{p+h} - \theta_p),$$

since

$$|x_k - x| = |\cos \theta_k - \cos \theta| \leqq \theta_k - \theta \leqq \theta_{p+h} - \theta_p.$$

But now $\theta_{p+h} - \theta_p = \dfrac{h\pi}{n}$.   For the value k in question therefore

$$|A_k - f(x)| \leqq \omega\left(\frac{h\pi}{n}\right).$$

From Lemma 2, § 3, Chapter II moreover

$$\frac{1}{n}\left|\frac{\cos n\theta}{\cos \theta - \cos \theta_k}\right|\sin \theta_k \leqq 2. \qquad (170)$$

The sum of those summands of $\tau'_n(x)$ the index k of which is not a multiple of $2l$ is therefore not greater than

$$2h\omega\left(\frac{h\pi}{n}\right)$$

(since the number of such k is not greater than h).

If however $k = 2ls$, then

$$|A_{2ls} - f(x)| \leqq |f(x_{2l(s-1)+1}) - f(x_{2l(s-1)+2})|$$
$$+ \cdots + |f(x_{2ls-3}) - f(x_{2ls-2})| + |f(x_{2ls-1}) - f(x)|.$$

Since $|x_{k+1} - x_k| \leqq \theta_{k+1} - \theta_k = \dfrac{\pi}{n}$, each summand of the righthand side—

excepting the last—is no greater than $\omega\left(\dfrac{\pi}{n}\right)$; the last is no greater than $\omega(|\theta_{2ls-1} - \theta|)$.

Now

$$\theta_p \leqq \theta < \theta_{p+1}, \quad \theta_{p+1} \leqq \theta_{2ls} \leqq \theta_{p+h}.$$

From the second inequality it follows that

$$\theta_p \leqq \theta_{2ls-1} \leqq \theta_{p+h-1};$$

hence

$$|\theta_{2ls-1} - \theta| \leqq \theta_{p+h-1} - \theta_p = \frac{h-1}{n}\pi < \frac{h\pi}{n},$$

and therefore

$$|A_{2ls} - f(x)| \leqq (l-1)\omega\left(\frac{\pi}{n}\right) + \omega\left(\frac{h\pi}{n}\right) \leqq l\omega\left(\frac{h\pi}{n}\right).$$

If we take the estimate (170) into account and note that there are at most $\dfrac{h-1}{2l}+1$ multiples of $2l$ among the numbers $p+1,\ p+2,\ \ldots,\ p+h$,[10]

then clearly the sum of those summands of $\tau'_n(x)$ which are divisible by $2l$ is not greater than

$$\left(\frac{h-1}{2l}+1\right)2l\omega\left(\frac{h\pi}{n}\right) < (h+2l)\omega\left(\frac{h\pi}{n}\right).$$

This together with the preceding remarks implies that

$$|\tau'_n(x)| < (3h+2l)\omega\left(\frac{h\pi}{n}\right). \tag{171}$$

Now let us consider the sum

$$\tau''_n(x) = \frac{1}{n}\sum_{k=p+h+1}^{n}(-1)^{k+1}[A_k - f(x)]\frac{\cos n\theta}{\cos\theta - \cos\theta_k}\sin\theta_k.$$

We first split off a partial sum S_s of $2l$ summands with indices

$$k = 2l(s-1)+1,\quad 2l(s-1)+2,\ \ldots,\ 2ls-1,\quad 2ls. \tag{172}$$

Using the notation

$$f(x_k) = f_k,\quad f(x) = f,\quad \frac{\sin\theta_k}{\cos\theta - \cos\theta_k} = u_k$$

the part of $\tau''_n(x)$ in question becomes

$$S_s = \frac{\cos n\theta}{n}\sum_{k=2l(s-1)+1}^{2ls-1}(-1)^{k+1}(f_k - f)\,u_k$$
$$-\frac{\cos n\theta}{n}\{[f_{2l(s-1)+1} + f_{2l(s-1)+3} + \cdots + f_{2ls-1}]$$
$$- [f_{2l(s-1)+2} + \cdots + f_{2ls-2}] - f\}u_{2ls}$$

or equivalently

$$S_s = \frac{\cos n\theta}{n}\left\{\sum(-1)^k f u_k + \sum(-1)^{k+1}f_k(u_k - u_{2ls})\right\},$$

[10] If these are the numbers

$$2l(i+1),\quad 2l(i+2),\ \ldots,\ 2l(i+m),$$

then the number of them is m. But now

$$2l(i+m) \leqq p+h,\quad 2l(i+1) \geqq p+1,$$

whence it follows that

$$2l(m-1) \leqq h-1.$$

where the summation is over all summands (172). From this it follows that

$$|S_s| \leqq \frac{M}{n} \{|\sum (-1)^k u_k| + \sum |u_k - u_{2ls}|\}, \tag{173}$$

where $M = \max |f(x)|$. Noting that the positive quantities

$$u_k = \frac{\sin \theta_k}{\cos \theta - \cos \theta_k}$$

decrease with increasing k,[11] we find

$$\begin{aligned} |\sum (-1)^k u_k| &= (u_{2l(s-1)+1} - u_{2l(s-1)+2}) + \cdots + (u_{2ls-1} - u_{2ls}) \\ &= u_{2l(s-1)+1} - (u_{2l(s-1)+2} - u_{2l(s-1)+3}) - \cdots \\ &\qquad - (u_{2ls-2} - u_{2ls-1}) - u_{2ls}, \end{aligned}$$

whence it follows that

$$|\sum (-1)^k u_k| \leqq u_{2l(s-1)+1} - u_{2ls}. \tag{174}$$

Now all of the differences $u_k - u_{2ls}$ are positive and none of them is greater than $u_{2l(s-1)+1} - u_{2ls}$; hence

$$\sum |u_k - u_{2ls}| < (2l - 1)(u_{2l(s-1)+1} - u_{2ls}).$$

From this, (173), and (174) it follows that

$$|S_s| \leqq \frac{2Ml}{n} (u_{2l(s-1)+1} - u_{2ls}).$$

Now suppose that there are sets of the form (172) with $s = \mu, \mu + 1, \ldots, \lambda$ in the sequence of numbers $p + h + 1, p + h + 2, \ldots, n$. This sequence may contain a certain number of elements which cannot be combined to a set of the form (172). The number of such indices k which do not belong to a set of the type (172) is however always less than $4l$. Since now $|A_k| \leqq (2l - 1)M$, the part of the sum $\tau_n''(x)$ corresponding to these particular values is less than

$$\frac{2lM}{n} \sum_{k \in Q} u_k,$$

where Q denotes the set of these particular values of k. Hence

$$|\tau_n''(x)| \leqq \frac{2Ml}{n} \left\{ \sum_{s=\mu}^{\lambda} [u_{2l(s-1)+1} - u_{2ls}] + \sum_{k \in Q} u_k \right\}.$$

[11] For

$$\left(\frac{\sin x}{\cos \theta - \cos x}\right)' = \frac{\cos \theta \cos x - 1}{(\cos \theta - \cos x)^2} < 0.$$

But now

$$\sum_{s=\mu}^{\lambda} [u_{2l(s-1)+1} - u_{2ls}] = u_{2l(\mu-1)+1} - (u_{2l\mu} - u_{2l\mu+1}) - \cdots$$
$$- (u_{2l(\lambda-1)} - u_{2l(\lambda-1)+1}) - u_{2l\lambda} < u_{2l(\mu-1)+1},$$

and therefore

$$|\tau_n''(x)| \leqq \frac{2Ml}{n} \left\{ u_{2l(\mu-1)+1} + \sum_{k \in Q} u_k \right\}.$$

All indices k occurring here are not less than $p + h + 1$. Taking into consideration the fact that u_k decreases with increasing k, we obtain

$$|\tau_n''(x)| \leqq \frac{8Ml^2}{n} u_{p+h+1}.$$

It remains to estimate u_{p+h+1}. Now

$$u_{p+h+1} = \frac{\sin \theta_{p+h+1}}{\cos \theta - \cos \theta_{p+h+1}} < \frac{\sin \theta_{p+h+1}}{\cos \theta_{p+1} - \cos \theta_{p+h+1}},$$

and hence

$$u_{p+h+1} < \frac{\sin \theta_{p+1} + \sin \theta_{p+h+1}}{\cos \theta_{p+1} - \cos \theta_{p+h+1}}$$
$$= \frac{2 \sin \frac{\theta_{p+1} + \theta_{p+h+1}}{2} \cos \frac{\theta_{p+h+1} - \theta_{p+1}}{2}}{2 \sin \frac{\theta_{p+1} + \theta_{p+h+1}}{2} \sin \frac{\theta_{p+h+1} - \theta_{p+1}}{2}};$$

from this it follows that

$$u_{p+h+1} < \frac{1}{\sin \frac{\theta_{p+h+1} - \theta_{p+1}}{2}}.$$

Noting that $\theta_{p+h+1} - \theta_{p+1} = \dfrac{h\pi}{n}$, we have

$$u_{p+h+1} < \frac{1}{\sin \frac{h\pi}{2n}} < \frac{n}{h}$$

and hence

$$|\tau_n''(x)| < \frac{8Ml^2}{h}.$$

This together with inequality (171) gives (note that $h > 2l$)

$$|\tau_n(x)| \leqq 4h\omega\left(\frac{h\pi}{n}\right) + \frac{8Ml^2}{h}.$$

This same estimate also holds for the sum

$$\frac{\cos n\theta}{n} \sum_{k=1}^{p} (-1)^{k+1}[A_k - f(x)]\frac{\sin\theta_k}{\cos\theta - \cos\theta_k};$$

hence

$$|P_n(x) - f(x)| < 8h\omega\left(\frac{h\pi}{n}\right) + \frac{16Ml^2}{h}.$$

Given $\varepsilon > 0$, we now choose h so large that

$$\frac{16Ml^2}{h} < \frac{\varepsilon}{2},$$

and then choose n so large that

$$8h\omega\left(\frac{h\pi}{n}\right) < \frac{\varepsilon}{2}.$$

This gives

$$|P_n(x) - f(x)| < \varepsilon,$$

wherewith (169) is proved.

§5. Certain General Properties of Summation Formulas

In this section we shall study certain properties of so-called summation formulas.   Let two triangular matrices be given: the matrix of "nodes"

$$\left.\begin{aligned} & x_1^{(1)}, \\ & x_1^{(2)}, \quad x_2^{(2)}, \\ & \cdots\cdots\cdots\cdots\cdots \\ & x_1^{(n)}, \quad x_2^{(n)}, \quad \ldots, \quad x_n^{(n)}, \\ & \cdots\cdots\cdots\cdots\cdots \end{aligned}\right\} \tag{175}$$

and the matrix of "basis functions"

$$\left.\begin{aligned} & \varphi_1^{(1)}(x), \\ & \varphi_1^{(2)}(x), \quad \varphi_2^{(2)}(x), \\ & \cdots\cdots\cdots\cdots\cdots \\ & \varphi_1^{(n)}(x), \quad \varphi_2^{(n)}(x), \quad \ldots, \quad \varphi_n^{(n)}(x), \\ & \cdots\cdots\cdots\cdots\cdots\cdots \end{aligned}\right\}, \tag{176}$$

where all nodes $x_k^{(n)}$ lie in the interval $[a, b]$ which is also the domain of definition of the functions $\varphi_k^{(n)}(x)$.

Under these conditions we can associate with every function $f(x)$ defined on $[a, b]$ a "summation polynomial"

$$\Phi_n(x) = \Phi_n[f; x] = \sum_{k=1}^{n} f(x_k^{(n)}) \varphi_k^{(n)}(x). \tag{177}$$

The concept of the summation polynomial thus contains that of a LAGRANGE interpolation polynomial as a special case but is considerably more general. Thus, for example, the BERNSTEIN polynomials

$$B_n(x) = \sum_{k=0}^{n} f\left(\frac{k}{n}\right) C_n^k x^k (1 - x)^{n-k}$$

and the FEJÉR polynomials

$$H_{2n-1}(x) = \sum_{k=1}^{n} f(x_k^{(n)}) \left(\frac{T_n(x)}{n(x - x_k^{(n)})}\right)^2 (1 - xx_k^{(n)})$$

are summation polynomials.

If we disregard the (inessential) condition that the nth row of the above matrices contains exactly n elements, then the trigonometric polynomials and the polynomials obtained from them in various manners are summation polynomials also. All theorems pertaining to summation polynomials therefore have a notable degree of generality. We shall, without making further mention of the fact, assume all basis functions $\varphi_k^{(n)}(x)$ to be individually bounded (not necessarily uniformly bounded by one and the same number).

With each pair of matrices (175) and (176) we associate the functions

$$\lambda_n(x) = \sum_{k=1}^{n} |\varphi_k^{(n)}(x)|$$

and the numbers

$$\lambda_n = \sup \{\lambda_n(x)\} \qquad (a \leqq x \leqq b).$$

Theorem 1. *The relation*

$$\lim_{n \to \infty} \Phi_n(x) = f(x) \tag{178}$$

holds uniformly on $[a, b]$ for every function $f(x) \, \epsilon \, C([a, b])$ if and only if
  1. *relation (178) holds uniformly for every polynomial* [12] *$f(x)$ and in addition*
  2. *there exists a constant K such that for all n*

$$\lambda_n \leqq K.$$

[12] The requirement that $f(x)$ be a polynomial may be replaced by the condition that $f(x)$ belong to a particular class of functions which is dense in $C([a, b])$

Proof. That the conditions are sufficient is almost obvious. Let us assume that they are satisfied, and let $f(x)$ be a function of the class $C([a, b])$. Given $\varepsilon > 0$, we choose a polynomial $P(x)$ such that

$$|P(x) - f(x)| < \varepsilon.$$

It is easily seen that

$$|\Phi_n[P; x] - \Phi_n[f; x]| = |\Phi_n[P - f; x]| < K\varepsilon.$$

From this and the inequality

$$|\Phi_n[f; x] - f(x)| \leqq |\Phi_n[f; x] - \Phi_n[P; x]| \\ + |\Phi_n[P; x] - P(x)| + |P(x) - f(x)|$$

one obtains the inequality

$$|\Phi_n[f; x] - f(x)| < (K + 1)\varepsilon + |\Phi_n[P; x] - P(x)|,$$

whence from condition 1 for sufficiently large n

$$|\Phi_n[f; x] - f(x)| < (K + 2)\varepsilon.$$

Now let us study the necessity of conditions 1 and 2. We see first of all that the necessity of condition 1 is trivial: if relation (178) holds for every continuous function, then it holds *a fortiori* for every polynomial. We obtain the necessity of condition 2 through the indirect method of the "sliding hump" similar to that used in the proof of the FABER theorem in Chapter II.

We assume that the relation (178) holds uniformly for all continuous functions, but that condition 2 does not hold. For every index n we then find a point z_n such that

$$\lambda_n(z_n) > \lambda_n - 1.$$

For every natural number n we now construct a function $\psi_n(x)$ by setting

$$\psi_n(x_k^{(n)}) = \operatorname{sign} \varphi_k^{(n)}(z_n) \qquad (k = 1, 2, \ldots, n)$$

and requiring that it be linear between the individual nodes and the end points of the interval $[a, b]$; at the end points we set the function $\psi_n(x)$ equal to zero if it is not already otherwise defined there by the above formula.

We now choose a number n_1 such that

$$\lambda_{n_1} > 2 \cdot 2 \cdot 3;$$

this is possible since condition 2 is not satisfied.

Since $\psi_{n_1}(x)$ is continuous, by hypothesis

$$\Phi_n\left[\frac{\psi_{n_1}}{3} ; x\right] \xrightarrow{\rightarrow} \frac{\psi_{n_1}(x)}{3},$$

and hence for all $n > n'$

$$\left| \Phi_n\left[\frac{\psi_{n_1}}{3} ; x \right] \right| < \frac{1}{2}$$

everywhere in $[a, b]$.

Now let $n_2 > n'$, $n_2 > n_1$ and in addition

$$\lambda_{n_2} > 2 \cdot 3 \cdot 3^2.$$

Since

$$\left| \frac{\psi_{n_1}(x)}{3} + \frac{\psi_{n_2}(x)}{3^2} \right| < \frac{1}{2},$$

there exists an $n_3 > n_2$ such that

$$\left| \Phi_{n_3}\left[\frac{\psi_{n_1}}{3} + \frac{\psi_{n_2}}{3^2} ; x \right] \right| < \frac{1}{2} \qquad \lambda_{n_3} > 2 \cdot 4 \cdot 3^3.$$

Continuing this process, we construct an infinite sequence $n_1 < n_2 < n_3 < \cdots$, for which the inequalities

$$\left| \Phi_{n_m}\left[\frac{\psi_{n_1}}{3} + \cdots + \frac{\psi_{n_{m-1}}}{3^{m-1}} ; x \right] \right| < \frac{1}{2},$$

$$\lambda_{n_m} > 2(m + 1)3^m$$

hold.   If we now put

$$f(x) = \sum_{k=1}^{\infty} \frac{\psi_{n_k}(x)}{3^k},$$

then $f(x)$ is obviously continuous in $[a, b]$.   If we moreover set

$$A(x) = \sum_{k=1}^{m-1} \frac{\psi_{n_k}(x)}{3^k}, \qquad B(x) = \sum_{k=m+1}^{\infty} \frac{\psi_{n_k}(x)}{3^k},$$

then

$$\Phi_{nm}[f; x] \geqq \frac{\Phi_{nm}[\psi_{nm}; x]}{3^m} - |\Phi_{nm}[A; x]| - |\Phi_{nm}[B; x]|.$$

By construction

$$|\Phi_{nm}[A; x]| < \frac{1}{2}.$$

Further

$$\left| \Phi_{nm}[B; x] \right| = \left| \sum_{k=1}^{nm} B(x_k^{(nm)}) \varphi_k^{(nm)}(x) \right| \leqq \lambda_{nm} \max |B(x)|,$$

and since

$$|B(x)| \leqq \frac{1}{3^{m+1}} + \frac{1}{3^{m+2}} + \frac{1}{3^{m+3}} + \cdots = \frac{1}{2 \cdot 3^m}$$

we obtain

$$\left| \Phi_{nm}[B; x] \right| \leqq \frac{\lambda_{nm}}{2 \cdot 3^m}.$$

Finally,

$$\Phi_{nm}[\psi_{nm}; z_{nm}] = \sum_{k=1}^{nm} \varphi_{nm}(x_k^{(nm)}) \varphi_k^{(nm)}(z_{nm}) = \lambda_{nm}(z_{nm}) > \lambda_{nm} - 1$$

and hence

$$\Phi_{nm}[f; z_{nm}] > \frac{\lambda_{nm} - 1}{3^m} - \frac{1}{2} - \frac{\lambda_{nm}}{2 \cdot 3^m};$$

therefore

$$\Phi_{nm}[f; z_{nm}] > \frac{\lambda_{nm}}{2 \cdot 3^m} - 1 > m.$$

The polynomial $\Phi_n[f; x]$ therefore does not converge uniformly to $f(x)$, wherewith the theorem is completely proved.

This theorem may without difficulty be carried over to the class of functions $C_{2\pi}$; one has only to alter the first condition by substituting trigonometric polynomials for ordinary algebraic polynomials.

In practice, the following convergence criterion is sometimes more suitable:

Theorem 2.   *In order that the relation*

$$\lim_{n \to \infty} \Phi_n(x) = f(x)$$

hold uniformly on $[a, b]$ for every function $f(x) \; \epsilon \; C([a, b])$ it is sufficient that in addition to condition 2 of Theorem 1 the following conditions be satisfied:

1′. as n becomes arbitrarily large

$$\sum_{k=1}^{n} \varphi_k^{(n)}(x) \rightrightarrows 1;$$

1″. *if the set of all k of the sequence $1, 2, 3, \ldots n$ such that $|x_k^{(n)} - x| \geqq \delta$ be deonoted by $\Delta_n(x, \delta)$, then there exists a function $\alpha_n(\delta)$ which for fixed δ tends to zero with increasing n and such that in addition*

$$\sum_{k \epsilon \Delta_n(x, \delta)} |\varphi_k^{(n)}(x)| < \alpha_n(\delta).$$

Proof. Suppose these conditions satisfied. If $f(x) \, \epsilon \, C([a, b])$, then

$$|\Phi_n[f; x] - f(x)| \leqq \left| \Phi_n[f; x] - f(x) \sum_{k=1}^{n} \varphi_k^{(n)}(x) \right| + |f(x)| \left| \sum_{k=1}^{n} \varphi_k^{(n)}(x) - 1 \right|.$$

According to condition 1′ the second summand of the righthand side tends uniformly to zero; we have therefore only to convince ourselves that the sum

$$\sum_{k=1}^{n} [f(x_k^{(n)}) - f(x)]\varphi_k^{(n)}(x) \tag{179}$$

also converges uniformly to zero.

Given $\varepsilon > 0$ we choose $\delta > 0$ such that $|x'' - x'| < \delta$ implies $|f(x'') - f(x')| < \varepsilon$; we then decompose the sum (179) into two sums $\sum_1$ and $\sum_2$ whereby all summands for whose index the inequality $|x_k^{(n)} - x| < \delta$ is satisfied belong to $\sum_1$ and all others belong to $\sum_2$. One easily finds the estimates

$$|\textstyle\sum_1| \leqq \varepsilon \lambda_n, \quad |\textstyle\sum_2| \leqq 2M\alpha_n(\delta),$$

where $M = \max |f(x)|$. The sum (179) is therefore less than

$$K\varepsilon + 2M\alpha_n(\delta);$$

the rest is clear.

Moreover, condition 1′ is (of course) also necessary for (178); for condition 1″ this is however not the case. This is shown by the following

Example. Let $a = 0, b = 1$

$$x_k^{(n)} = \frac{k}{n}, \quad \varphi_k^{(n)}(x) = C_n^k x^k (1 - x)^{n-k} + \tau_k \quad (k = 0, 1, \ldots, n),$$

where

$$\tau_0 = 1, \quad \tau_1 = -1, \quad \tau_2 = \tau_3 = \cdots = \tau_n = 0.$$

One readily sees that

$$\Phi_n[f; x] = B_n[f; x] + f(0) - f\left(\frac{1}{n}\right),$$

where $B_n[f; x]$ is the BERNSTEIN polynomial of the function $f(x)$. From this it follows easily that (178) holds. However for $\delta = \dfrac{1}{3}$

$$\sum_{k \in \Delta_n(\frac{1}{3}, \frac{1}{2})} \left| \varphi_k^{(n)} \left(\frac{1}{2} \right) \right| > \left| \varphi_0^{(n)} \left(\frac{1}{2} \right) \right| + \left| \varphi_1^{(n)} \left(\frac{1}{2} \right) \right| = 2 - \frac{n-1}{2^n},$$

so that condition $1''$ is not satisfied.[13]

Finally, we prove

Theorem 3. *If the summation polynomial has the property that for every polynomial $P_n(x)$ of H_n the identity*

$$\Phi_n[P_n; x] \equiv P_n(x) \tag{180}$$

holds, then the relation

$$\lim_{n \to \infty} \Phi_n(x) = f(x)$$

holds uniformly on $[a, b]$ for every function $f(x)$ whose best approximation $E_n(f)$ by polynomials of H_n satisfies the condition

$$\lim_{n \to \infty} \lambda_n E_n(f) = 0$$

Proof. Let $f(x)$ be such a function and $P(x)$ be its polynomial of best approximation. Then

$$|\Phi_n[f; x] - f(x)| \leqq |\Phi_n[f - P_n; x]| + |P_n(x) - f(x)| \leqq (\lambda_n + 1)E_n(f),$$

wherewith the theorem is proved.

Condition (180) is stronger than condition 1 of Theorem 1; however, it is not required that the numbers λ_n be bounded.

---

[13] S. J. RAPPOPORT has proved that condition $1''$ becomes a necessary condition for the uniform convergence of $\Phi_n(x)$ to $f(x)$ if all the basis functions $\varphi_k^{(n)}(x)$ are non-negative.

CHAPTER V

APPROXIMATION QUADRATURES

§1. The Problem

Let $f(x)$ be a continuous function on the interval $[a, b]$; it is then required to calculate the definite integral

$$\int_a^b f(x)\, dx. \tag{181}$$

If it is possible to find a primitive function $F(x)$ of $f(x)$, then the problem has the classical solution given by NEWTON and LEIBNITZ:

$$\int_a^b f(x)\, dx = F(b) - F(a).$$

Very often this formula cannot be used, since a primitive function is not known. In such cases one is forced to seek other ways of calculating the integral (181). One such way is as follows: we choose n arbitrary points $x_1, x_2, \ldots, x_n$ and construct the LAGRANGE interpolation polynomial $L(x)$ which coincides with $f(x)$ at the points x_k:

$$L(x) = \sum_{k=1}^n f(x_k) l_k(x).$$

If $f(x)$ is a well-behaved (e.g. entire) function we may regard the polynomial $L(x)$ as an approximation function for it and instead of the integral (181) compute the following:

$$\int_a^b L(x)\, dx = \sum_{k=1}^n f(x_k) \int_a^b l_k(x)\, dx.$$

If we set

$$\int_a^b l_k(x)\, dx = A_k,$$

then our approximation formula reads

$$\int_a^b f(x)\, dx \approx \sum_{k=1}^n A_k f(x_k). \tag{182}$$

Formulas of this type are called *formulas for approximation quadratures*. They may assume very different forms, depending on the number of nodes. An important point is that since

$$l_k(x) = \frac{(x - x_1)\cdots(x - x_{k-1})(x - x_{k+1})\cdots(x - x_n)}{(x_k - x_1)\cdots(x_k - x_{k-1})(x_k - x_{k+1})\cdots(x_k - x_n)}$$

the coefficients A_k do not depend on the function $f(x)$ to be integrated. This fact has the following practical application: suppose that we have many integrals of the form (181) to compute over the same interval $[a, b]$ with pairwise different integrands; then can first choose nodes x_k, compute the coefficients A_k, and only then use formula (182) for the various functions $f(x)$. This considerably reduces the work in computation

As an example we derive the so-called "trapezoid formula". If we choose $n = 2$ and as nodes the two endpoints of the interval $[a, b]$, then we obtain the LAGRANGE polynomial

$$L(x) = \frac{x - b}{a - b}f(a) + \frac{x - a}{b - a}f(b).$$

Since

$$\int_a^b \frac{x - b}{a - b}\,dx = \int_a^b \frac{x - a}{b - a}\,dx = \frac{b - a}{2}$$

formula (182) becomes

$$\int_a^b f(x)\,dx = \frac{b - a}{2}[f(a) + f(b)] \qquad (183)$$

which is just the *trapezoid formula*.

If the integrand $f(x)$ has one (or more) derivative, then one may use the HERMITE polynomials rather than the LAGRANGE interpolation polynomials. In general this leads to quadrature formulas in which the values of the derivatives of the function at the nodal points as well as the values of the function itself occur. However, the terms containing the values of the derivatives may vanish, in which case we again obtain formulas of the form (182). An interesting example of this type is the so-called "SIMPSON formula". To derive this formula we set

$$c = \frac{a + b}{2}$$

and construct the HERMITE polynomial $H(x)$ from the conditions [1]

$$H(a) = f(a), \ H(c) = f(c), \ H'(c) = f'(c), \ H(b) = f(b). \qquad (184)$$

According to § 4, Chapter I, we must introduce three polynomials

$$P_1(x) = A, \quad P_2(x) = B, \quad P_3(x) = C_1 + C_2(x - c)$$

and then set

$$H(x) = A + B(x - a) + (x - a)(x - b)[C_1 + C_2(x - c)]. \qquad (185)$$

We now determine the coefficients A, B, C_1, C_2 such that conditions (184) are satisfied.

Putting $x = a$, we obtain immediately $A = f(a)$. Using this value for A and putting $x = b$, we find

$$B = \frac{f(b) - f(a)}{b - a}.$$

Now putting $x = c$ in (185), we obtain

$$C_1 = 2\frac{f(a) + f(b) - 2f(c)}{(b - a)^2}.$$

Now as for the coefficient C_2, the expression for it will contain the quantity $f'(c)$; however, this coefficient does not (as we shall see) appear in the final formula. We shall therefore not compute it.

Putting

$$\int\limits_a^b f(x)\, dx = \int\limits_a^b H(x)\, dx$$

and using formula (185), we obtain

$$\int\limits_a^b f(x)\, dx = A \int\limits_a^b dx + B \int\limits_a^b (x - a)\, dx + C_1 \int\limits_a^b (x - a)(x - b)\, dx$$

$$+ C_2 \int\limits_a^b (x - a)(x - b)(x - c)\, dx.$$

---

[1] We thus assume the existence of $f'(x)$ at least at the point $x = c$.

Now [2]

$$\int_a^b dx = b - a, \qquad \int_a^b (x - a)\, dx = \frac{(b - a)^2}{2},$$

$$\int_a^b (x - a)(x - b)\, dx = -\frac{(b - a)^3}{6},$$

$$\int_a^b (x - a)(x - b)(x - c)\, dx = 0.$$

Hence

$$\int_a^b f(x)\, dx = \frac{b - a}{6}\, [f(a) + 4f(c) + f(b)], \tag{186}$$

and this is the SIMPSON *formula*.

This train of thought quite naturally leads us to a number of problems. The first question arising is whether there exists a system of nodes which gives the integral of *every* continuous function over the designated path to arbitrary accuracy.

Recalling that there does not exist a matrix of nodes giving rise to a uniformly convergent interpolation process for all continuous functions, it would seem at first glance that this question should be answered negatively. However, the situation is actually quite different. As we shall presently see, the roots of the LEGENDRE polynomials $X_n(x)$ afford in the interval $[-1, +1]$ a system of nodes for which the approximation formula (182) with increasing n becomes as accurate as desired for *every* continuous function.

One will also of course seek to establish the magnitude of the error in formula (182) when particular conditions are imposed on the function $f(x)$. Finally, there arises the question of the best choice of nodes; this may refer to either greatest possible accuracy of the approximation (182) or simplest possible computation of the coefficients A_k.

We shall henceforth be concerned with these and other questions related to the study of formula (182).

---

[2] The first two equations are obvious. To compute the third and fourth integrals it is expedient to use the substitution $x = c + t\,\dfrac{b - a}{2}$. Thus for example

$$\int_a^b (x - a)(x - b)(x - c)\, dx = \frac{(b - a)^4}{16} \int_{-1}^{+1} t(t^2 - 1)\, dt = 0,$$

since the integrand is an odd function of t.

§2. The Remainder in the Quadrature Formula

If the function $f(x)$ has continuous derivatives through nth order (where n is the number of nodes x_k), then as we proved in Chapter I the exact formula

$$f(x) = L(x) + \frac{f^{(n)}(\xi)}{n!}\,\omega(x) \qquad\qquad (a < \xi < b)$$

holds where $\omega(x) = (x - x_1)(x - x_2)\ldots(x - x_n)$. From this it follows that

$$\int_a^b f(x)\,dx = \sum_{k=1}^n A_k f(x_k) + \frac{1}{n!}\int_a^b f^{(n)}(\xi)\omega(x)\,dx. \qquad (187)$$

A precise computation of the remainder involves great complications, since we do not know the dependence of ξ on x; however, an estimate of the remainder is not difficult. If

$$M_n = \max\, |\, f^{(n)}(x)\,|,$$

then clearly [3]

$$\left|\, \int_a^b f(x)\,dx - \sum_{k=1}^n A_k f(x_k)\, \right| \leq \frac{M_n}{n!}\int_a^b |\,\omega(x)\,|\,dx. \qquad (188)$$

From this it is evident that with arbitrary choice of nodes for every entire function $f(x)$ the equality

$$\lim_{n\to\infty} \sum_{k=1}^n A_k f(x_k) = \int_a^b f(x)\,dx$$

holds as the number of nodes becomes infinite.[4] If we use a quadrature formula formed by integrating a HERMITE polynomial $H_n(x)$ constructed from the conditions

$$H^{(i)}(x_k) = f^{(i)}(x_k)$$
$$(k = 1, 2, \ldots, n;\ i = 0, 1, \ldots, a_k - 1),$$

[3] According to the theorem of KORKIN and ZOLATAREV (Vol. II, Ch. VI, § 4), the factor $\int_a^b |\,\omega(x)\,|\,dx$ attains its minimum if we choose the roots of the polynomial

$$\frac{\sin\,(n + 1)\,\mathrm{arc\,cos}\,\dfrac{2x - (a + b)}{b - a}}{\sqrt{(x - a)(b - x)}}$$

as interpolation nodes.

[4] Since $\int_a^b |\,\omega(x)\,|\,dx \leq (b - a)^{n+1}$, and for an entire function $\lim_{n\to\infty} \dfrac{M_n(b - a)^r}{n!} = 0$.

then the error is not greater than

$$\frac{M_m}{m!} \int_a^b |\Omega(x)|\ dx,$$ (189)

where $m = a_1 + a_2 + \cdots + a_n$, $M_m = \max |f^{(m)}(x)|$, and [5]

$$\Omega(x) = (x - x_1)^{a_1}(x - x_2)^{a_2} \cdots (x - x_n)^{a_n}.$$

If the function $\Omega(x)$ does not change sign in $[a, b]$ (which is the case for example when all the exponents $a_1, a_2, \ldots, a_n$ are even numbers), then the upper bound (189) may be replaced by the exact expression for the remainder

$$\frac{f^{(m)}(\xi)}{m!} \int_a^b \Omega(x)\ dx \qquad (a \le \xi \le b).$$ (190)

Since ξ is unknown, (190) again gives the estimate (189); moreover, it is now evident that the order of magnitude of this estimate cannot be improved, since the bound (189) is actually attained for all functions whose mth derivative is a constant. If the function $\omega(x)$ does not change sign in $[a, b]$, then formula (187) can also be written

$$\int_a^b f(x)\ dx = \sum_{k=1}^n A_k f(x_k) + \frac{f^{(n)}(\xi)}{n!} \int_a^b \omega(x)\ dx.$$ (191)

As examples, let us examine the remainders for the trapezoid formula and for SIMPSON's formula.

In the trapzoid formula $n = 2$ and $\omega(x) = (x - a)(x - b)$. Since $\omega(x)$ does not change sign in $[a, b]$ and since [6]

$$\int_a^b (x - a)(x - b)\ dx = -\frac{(b - a)^3}{6},$$

we obtain

$$\int_a^b f(x)\ dx = \frac{b - a}{2}[f(a) + f(b)] - \frac{(b - a)^3}{12} f''(\xi)$$ (192)

$$(a \le \xi \le b).$$

[5] If $a_1 = a_2 = \cdots = a_n = 2$, then $\int_a^b |\Omega(x)|\ dx$ assumes it minimum value when the nodes x_k are roots of the polynomial $X_n\left[\dfrac{2x - (a + b)}{b - a}\right]$, where $X_n(t)$ is the LEGENDRE polynomial.

[6] This integral is most easily computed by means of the substitution $x = a + t(b - a)$.

In SIMPSON's formula $n = 4$ and $\Omega(x) = (x - a)(x - c)^2(x - b)$ where $2c = a + b$. Here also the sign of $\Omega(x)$ does not change in $[a, b]$; from the fact that [7]

$$\int_a^b (x - a)(x - c)^2(x - b)\, dx = -\frac{(b - a)^5}{120},$$

we obtain

$$\int_a^b f(x)\, dx = \frac{b - a}{6}\,[f(a) + 4f(c) + f(b)] - \frac{(b - a)^5}{2880}\, f^{(4)}(\xi) \qquad (193)$$

$$(a \leqq \xi \leqq b).$$

In order to increase the accuracy of the quadrature formula, one can increase the number of nodes; the degree of the interpolation polynomial hereby increases correspondingly. In addition, one must also note the following: the law according to which new nodes are added is of the greatest importance; to be sure, for an entire function we obtain as indicated above an arbitrarily close approximation for any choice of nodes, but for an arbitrary continuous function this is no longer the case. Moreover, the construction of interpolation polynomials of higher orders is extremely complicated.

In practice one adopts quite another method in order to increase the accuracy of the quadrature formula: one partitions the interval of integration into several parts, then applies on each component interval a quadrature formula with only a few nodes, and finally adds the separate integrals so obtained.

We shall illustrate this procedure again with the trapezoid formula and SIMPSON's formula.

Let us assume that the interval $[a, b]$ is partitioned by the points

$$x_0 = a < x_1 < x_2 < \cdots < x_n = b$$

into intervals $[x_k, x_{k+1}]$ of equal lengths. Applying the trapezoid formula (183) to each interval $[x_k, x_{k+1}]$, we obtain n approximate equations

$$\int_{x_k}^{x_{k+1}} f(x)\, dx = \frac{b - a}{2n}\,(y_k + y_{k+1}) \qquad (k = 0, 1, 2, \ldots, n - 1), \quad (194)$$

where for brevity we have put $f(x_k) = y_k$. From this we obtain the "augmented" trapezoid formula

$$\int_a^b f(x)\, dx = \frac{b - a}{2n}\,[y_0 + 2(y_1 + y_2 + \cdots + y_{n-1}) + y_n]. \qquad (195)$$

---

[7] The substitution $x = c + \dfrac{b - a}{2}\, t$ is convenient.

We now determine the error of this formula. If we assume the existence of a continuous second derivative $f''(x)$, then the error in each of the terms (194) will be equal to

$$-\frac{(b-a)^3}{12n^3}f''(\xi_k) \qquad (x_k \leqq \xi_k \leqq x_{k+1}).$$

The total error in formula (195) will therefore be

$$-\frac{(b-a)^3}{12n^3}\sum_{k=0}^{n-1}f''(\xi_k).$$

The quantity

$$\frac{1}{n}\sum_{k=0}^{n-1}f''(\xi_k),$$

as is easily seen, lies between the maximum and minimum values of $f''(x)$ in $[a, b]$. Because of the continuity of $f''(x)$ in $[a, b]$ there therefore exists a point $\xi \epsilon [a, b]$ such that

$$f''(\xi) = \frac{1}{n}\sum_{k=0}^{n-1}f''(\xi_k);$$

hence

$$\int_a^b f(x)\,dx = \frac{b-a}{2n}[y_0 + 2(y_1 + y_2 + \cdots + y_{n-1}) + y_n] - \frac{(b-a)^3}{12n^2}f''(\xi)$$

$$(a \leqq \xi \leqq b) \qquad (196)$$

One has therefore according to formula (196) for every function $f(x)$ with continuous second derivative the equality

$$\lim_{n\to\infty}\frac{b-a}{2n}[y_0 + 2(y_1 + y_2 + \cdots + y_{n-1}) + y_n] = \int_a^b f(x)\,dx. \quad (197)$$

Moreover, the last equation (197) holds not only for such functions, but also for every R-integrable function, for the sum

$$\frac{b-a}{2n}[y_0 + 2(y_1 + y_2 + \cdots + y_{n-1}) + y_n]$$

is the arithmetic mean of the two RIEMANN sums

$$\left.\begin{array}{l}\sigma_1 = \dfrac{b-a}{n}(y_0 + y_1 + \cdots + y_{n-1}),\\[2em]\sigma_2 = \dfrac{b-a}{n}(y_1 + y_2 + \cdots + y_n),\end{array}\right\} \qquad (198)$$

each of which converges to $\displaystyle\int_a^b f(x)\,dx.$

If we now in an analogous way partition the interval $[a, b]$ into an even number n of subintervals $[x_i, x_{i+1}]$ and apply SIMPSON's formula to each double interval $[x_{2k}, x_{2k+2}]$, we obtain

$$\int_{x_{2k}}^{x_{2k+2}} f(x)\, dx = \frac{b-a}{3n} [y_{2k} + 4y_{2k+1} + y_{2k+2}] - \frac{(b-a)^5}{90n^5} f^{(4)}(\xi_k),$$

whence there results the "augmented" SIMPSON formula with remainder:

$$\int_a^b f(x)\, dx = \frac{b-a}{3n} [y_0 + 4(y_1 + y_3 + \cdots + y_{n-1})$$

$$+ 2(y_2 + y_4 + \cdots + y_{n-2}) + y_n] - \frac{(b-a)^5}{180n^4} f^{(4)}(\xi). \quad (199)$$

The occurrence of the power n^4 in the denominator of the remainder indicates a far greater accuracy of the SIMPSON formula [8] as compared with formula (196) wherein the denominator of the remainder contains only the factor n^2. This occurs in spite of the fact that the amount of computation in both cases is about the same (with the same number of nodes).

As above, we obtain for every integrable function the limit relation

$$\lim_{n \to \infty} \frac{b-a}{3n} [y_0 + 4(y_1 + y_3 + \cdots + y_{n-1})$$

$$+ 2(y_2 + y_4 + \cdots + y_{n-2}) + y_n] = \int_a^b f(x)\, dx. \quad (200)$$

If we put

$$\sigma_3 = \frac{2(b-a)}{n} (y_1 + y_3 + y_5 + \cdots + y_{n-1}),$$

then we have

$$\frac{b-a}{3n} [y_0 + 4(y_1 + y_3 + \cdots + y_{n-1})$$

$$+ 2(y_2 + y_4 + \cdots + y_{n-2}) + y_n] = \frac{\sigma_1 + \sigma_2 + \sigma_3}{3},$$

where σ_1 and σ_2 are defined by (198); it remains now only to remark that σ_3 is also a RIEMANN sum of the function corresponding to a partition of the interval $[a, b]$ by the points $x_0, x_2, x_4, \ldots, x_n$.

[8] We are not being precise here. Formulas (196) and (199) are not approximate but exact. We refer to the approximation formulas obtained from these by dropping the remainders.

§3. Quadratures of GAUSSIAN Type

The quadrature formula

$$\int_a^b f(x)\,dx = \sum_{k=1}^n A_k f(x_k) \tag{201}$$

is exact for an arbitrary choice of nodes whenever $f(x)$ is a polynomial from H_{n-1}, since in this case the function $f(x)$ is identical with its LAGRANGE interpolation polynomial. Moreover, the problem of specially choosing the nodes such that equation (201) be exact for all polynomials of the class H_{2n-1} was posed and solved by K. F. GAUSS [1]. His results were generalized by K. A. POSSE [1]. We shall here develope the theory of K. A. POSSE as well as extensions and supplements added thereto by A. A. MARKOFF [1, 2] and T. J. STIELTJES.

Let there be given on the interval $[a, b]$ a weight function $p(x) \geqq 0$ of which we require as heretofore that it be summable and vanish at most on a set of measure zero. We then choose nodes $x_1, x_2, \ldots, x_n$ in $[a, b]$ and construct for every continuous function $f(x)$ the LAGRANGE interpolation polynomial

$$L(x) = \sum_{k=1}^n f(x_k) l_k(x), \tag{202}$$

with the usual notation

$$l_k(x) = \frac{\omega(x)}{\omega'(x_k)(x - x_k)}, \qquad \omega(x) = \prod_{k=1}^n (x - x_k).$$

We now multiply (202) by $p(x)$ and integrate:

$$\int_a^b p(x) L(x)\,dx = \sum_{k=1}^n A_k f(x_k),$$

where

$$A_k = \int_a^b p(x) l_k(x)\,dx. \tag{203}$$

In view of the fact that $L(x)$ represents an approximation of $f(x)$, we obtain as the formula for an approximation quadrature

$$\int_a^b p(x) f(x)\,dx = \sum_{k=1}^n A_k f(x_k), \tag{204}$$

which—just as formula (201)—is exact whenever $f(x)$ is a polynomial of H_{n-1}. Our problem is now to find nodes x_k such that formula (204) remains exact when $f(x)$ is any polynomial of H_{2n-1}; the question raised by GAUSS is obviously a special case of this problem.

A system of nodes satisfying this condition will be called a *system of nodes of Gaussian type* or more briefly *"nodes of Gaussian type."*

Theorem 1. *The n nodes x_k are nodes of Gaussian type if and only if they are roots of a polynomial $\omega_n(x)$ of degree n which is orthogonal with weight $p(x)$ to all polynomials of H_{n-1}.*

Proof. Suppose that the nodes x_k are of Gaussian type. We define

$$\omega_n(x) = (x - x_1)(x - x_2) \cdots (x - x_n). \tag{205}$$

Now let $\theta(x)$ be a polynomial of H_{n-1}. The polynomial

$$f(x) = \theta(x)\omega_n(x)$$

then belongs to H_{2n-1}; therefore the equation

$$\int_a^b p(x)f(x)\, dx = \sum_{k=1}^n A_k f(x_k)$$

holds. But now $f(x_1) = f(x_2) = \cdots = f(x_n) = 0$, and hence

$$\int_a^b p(x)\theta(x)\omega_n(x)\, dx = 0,$$

so that $\omega_n(x)$ is orthogonal with weight $p(x)$ to $\theta(x)$. Since $\theta(x)$ was entirely arbitrary, the necessity of the condition is proved.

Now suppose conversely that the polynomial (205) is orthogonal with weight $p(x)$ to all polynomials of H_{n-1}.

Let $f(x)$ be an arbitrary polynomial of H_{2n-1}. Dividing $f(x)$ by $\omega_n(x)$, we obtain

$$f(x) = \theta(x)\omega_n(x) + \rho(x), \tag{206}$$

where both the quotient $\theta(x)$ and the remainder $\rho(x)$ are polynomials of H_{n-1}.

From this it follows that

$$\int_a^b p(x)f(x)\, dx = \int_a^b p(x)\theta(x)\omega_n(x)\, dx + \int_a^b p(x)\rho(x)\, dx.$$

By hypothesis the first integral on the righthand side vanishes, and therefore

$$\int\limits_a^b p(x)f(x)\,dx = \int\limits_a^b p(x)\rho(x)\,dx = \sum_{k=1}^n A_k\rho(x_k).$$

From (206) however we obtain $\rho(x_k) = f(x_k)$ $(k = 1, 2, \ldots, n)$; hence we have the exact equation

$$\int\limits_a^b p(x)f(x)\,dx = \sum_{k=1}^n A_kf(x_k),$$

so that the nodes x_k are indeed of GAUSSIAN type.

Corollary. *For* $a = -1$, $b = +1$, $p(x) = 1$ *the roots of the* LEGENDRE *polynomials* $X_n(x)$ *are a solution of* GAUSS's *problem.*

In addition we note that for arbitrary choice of nodes the coefficients A_k of formula (204) satisfy the equality

$$\sum_{k=1}^n A_k = \int\limits_a^b p(x)\,dx, \tag{207}$$

since formula (204) is valid for every polynomial of H_{n-1} and hence also for $f(x) = 1$.

If the nodes are of GAUSSIAN type, then we call the formula (204) a *formula of Gaussian type.* Then for the coefficients A_k we have in addition to (207) the

Lemma. *All coefficients of a formula of Gaussian type are positive.*

Proof. We substitute the function

$$f(x) = \left[\frac{\omega_n(x)}{x - x_i}\right]^2$$

into formula (204). Since this is a polynomial of degree $2n - 2$, we have the equality

$$\int\limits_a^b p(x)f(x)\,dx = \sum_{k=1}^n A_kf(x_k).$$

But now

$$f(x_k) = \begin{cases} 0, & \text{if } k \neq i; \\ [\omega_n'(x_i)]^2, & \text{if } k = i \end{cases}$$

and hence

$$\int\limits_a^b p(x)f(x)\,dx = A_i[\omega_n'(x_i)]^2.$$

From this it follows that

$$A_i = \int\limits_a^b p(x) \left[\frac{\omega_n(x)}{\omega_n'(x_i)(x - x_i)} \right]^2 dx, \qquad (208)$$

wherewith the lemma is proved.[9]

With the help of the lemma we can now easily prove

Theorem 2 (T. J. STIELTJES [1]). *Let $p(x)$ be a weight function and $\{\omega_n(x)\}$ an orthogonal system of polynomials with this weight. If $x_1^{(n)}, x_2^{(n)}, \ldots, x_n^{(n)}$ are the roots of the polynomial $\omega_n(x)$ and $A_1^{(n)}, A_2^{(n)}, \ldots, A_n^{(n)}$ are the coefficients of the quadrature formula (203) with the roots as nodes, then for every continuous function $f(x)$ the limit relation*

$$\lim_{n \to \infty} \sum_{k=1}^n A_k^{(n)} f(x_k^{(n)}) = \int\limits_a^b p(x)f(x)\, dx \qquad (209)$$

holds.

Proof. Because of the continuity of $f(x)$, given any $\varepsilon > 0$ there exists a polynomial $P(x)$ such that at all points $x \in [a, b]$ the inequality

$$|P(x) - f(x)| < \varepsilon \qquad (210)$$

holds. For brevity putting

$$Q_n(f) = \sum_{k=1}^n A_k^{(n)} f(x_k^{(n)}), \qquad (211)$$

we have

$$\left| \int\limits_a^b p(x)f(x)\, dx - Q_n(f) \right| \leqq \left| \int\limits_a^b p(x)f(x)\, dx - \int\limits_a^b p(x)P(x)\, dx \right|$$

$$+ \left| \int\limits_a^b p(x)P(x)\, dx - Q_n(P) \right| + |Q_n(P) - Q_n(f)|.$$

According to (210)

$$\left| \int\limits_a^b p(x)f(x)\, dx - \int\limits_a^b p(x)P(x)\, dx \right| \leqq \varepsilon \int\limits_a^b p(x)\, dx$$

and from (207) in addition

[9] We point out that $\omega_n'(x_i) \neq 0$, since x_i is a simple root of $\omega_n(x)$.

$$\left| Q_n(P) - Q_n(f) \right| = \left| \sum_{k=1}^{n} A_k^{(n)} \{ P(x_k^{(n)}) - f(x_k^{(n)}) \} \right| \leq \varepsilon \sum_{k=1}^{n} A_k^{(n)}$$

$$= \varepsilon \int_a^b p(x)\, dx.$$

Hence

$$\left| \int_a^b p(x)f(x)\, dx - Q_n(f) \right| \leq 2\varepsilon \int_a^b p(x)\, dx + \left| \int_a^b p(x)P(x)\, dx - Q_n(P) \right|.$$

If now m is the degree of the polynomial $P(x)$, then for $2n - 1 \geq m$

$$Q_n(P) = \int_a^b p(x)P(x)\, dx;$$

for this n therefore

$$\left| \int_a^b p(x)f(x)\, dx - Q_n(f) \right| \leq 2\varepsilon \int_a^b p(x)\, dx,$$

wherewith the theorem is proved.[10]

We note that the STIELTJES theorem in Chapter IV, § 3, Vol. II on the expansion of the integral

$$\int_a^b \frac{p(t)}{x - t}\, dt$$

in a continuous fraction now appears as a simple consequence of the theorem just proved. Indeed, if x lies outside the interval $[a, b]$ the function

$$f(t) = \frac{1}{x - t}$$

is continuous in $[a, b]$, and hence from (209)

$$\int_a^b \frac{p(t)}{x - t}\, dt = \lim_{n \to \infty} \sum_{k=1}^{n} \frac{A_k^{(n)}}{x - x_k^{(n)}}. \qquad (212)$$

Now (with the notation of § 3, Ch. IV, Vol. II)

---

[10] This theorem also follows directly from Theorem 3, § 3, Chapter III on the convergence of the LAGRANGE interpolation polynomials in mean.

$$A_k^{(n)} = \frac{1}{\omega_n'(x_k^{(n)})} \int_a^b p(t) \frac{\omega_n(t)}{t - x_k^{(n)}} dt = \frac{\psi_n(x_k^{(n)})}{\omega_n'(x_k^{(n)})},$$

and hence

$$\sum_{k=1}^{n} \frac{A_k^{(n)}}{x - x_k^{(n)}} = \sum_{k=1}^{n} \frac{\psi_n(x_k^{(n)})}{\omega_n'(x_k^{(n)})(x - x_k^{(n)})}.$$

The righthand side of this equality is the decomposition of the rational function

$$\frac{\psi_n(x)}{\omega_n(x)} = \frac{\psi_n(x)}{(x - x_1^{(n)})(x - x_2^{(n)}) \cdots (x - x_n^{(n)})}$$

into partial fractions.[11]   Hence

$$\sum_{k=1}^{n} \frac{A_k^{(n)}}{x - x_k^{(n)}} = \frac{\psi_n(x)}{\omega_n(x)},$$

so that (212) assumes the form

$$\int_a^b \frac{p(t)}{x - t} dt = \lim_{n \to \infty} \frac{\psi_n(x)}{\omega_n(x)}$$

This proof is certainly simpler than the one given in Volume II; it has however the disadvantage that it does not give the uniform convergence of the fraction $\frac{\psi_n(x)}{\omega_n(x)}$ to the value of the integral.

In conclusion we shall undertake an estimate of accuracy of the formulas of Gaussian type, whereby it is assumed that the function $f(x)$ has continuous derivatives through order $2n$.

If we construct the HERMITE interpolation polynomial $H(x)$ which is determined by the conditions

$$H(x_k) = f(x_k), \quad H'(x_k) = f'(x_k) \quad (k = 1, 2, \ldots, n),$$

[11] The formula

$$\frac{\psi_n(x)}{\omega_n(x)} = \sum_{k=1}^{n} \frac{c_k}{x - x_k^{(n)}}$$

is known from the elements of algebra. Multiplying this equation by $x - x_i^{(n)}$ and then setting $x = x_i^{(n)}$, we obtain

$$c_i = \frac{\psi_n(x_i^{(n)})}{\omega_n'(x_i^{(n)})}.$$

we obtain from the expansions of §4 in Chapter I

$$f(x) = H(x) + \frac{f^{(2n)}(\xi)}{(2n)!} (x - x_1)^2 (x - x_2)^2 \cdots (x - x_n)^2.$$

From this it follows that

$$\int_a^b p(x)f(x)\, dx = \int_a^b p(x)H(x)\, dx + \frac{1}{(2n)!} \int_a^b p(x)f^{(2n)}(\xi)\omega_n^2(x)\, dx.$$

Now the degree of $H(x)$ is at most $2n - 1$; hence

$$\int_a^b p(x)H(x)\, dx = Q_n(H) = Q_n(f).$$

Moreover, the factor $p(x)\omega_n^2(x)$ is positive. We therefore obtain finally [12]

$$\int_a^b p(x)f(x)\, dx = Q_n(f) + \frac{f^{(2n)}(\xi)}{(2n)!} \int_a^b p(x)\omega_n^2(x)\, dx, \tag{213}$$

a formula due to A. A. MARKOFF.

§4. Special Quadratures of GAUSSIAN Type

I. The GAUSS Formula.

If $p(x) = 1$, $a = -1$, $b = +1$, then as we have just seen the roots of the LEGENDRE polynomial $X_n(x)$ form a system of nodes of Gaussian type. Denoting these roots by $\xi_1^{(n)}, \xi_2^{(n)}, \ldots, \xi_n^{(n)}$ we obtain the quadrature formula

$$\int_{-1}^{+1} f(x)\, dx = \sum_{k=1}^{n} A_k^{(n)} f(\xi_k^{(n)}) \tag{214}$$

where

$$A_k^{(n)} = \frac{1}{X_n'(\xi_k^{(n)})} \int_{-1}^{+1} \frac{X_n(t)}{t - \xi_k^{(n)}}\, dt, \tag{215}$$

and (214) is an exact equation if $f(x) \, \epsilon \, H_{2n-1}$. This formula goes back to GAUSS himself.

[12] It should be pointed out here that in this section we mean by $\omega_n(x)$ that orthogonal polynomial with weight $p(x)$ whose leading coefficient is 1 (this polynomial was denoted by $\bar{\omega}_n(x)$ in Volume II).

From the general formula (213) of A. A. MARKOFF the remainder for formula (214) is

$$R_n = \frac{f^{(2n)}(\xi)}{(2n!)} \int_{-1}^{+1} \breve{X}_n^2(t)\, dt.$$

In § 1, Ch. V, Vol. II we proved that

$$\int_{-1}^{+1} \breve{X}_n^2(t)\, dt = 2\, \frac{[(2n)!!]^2}{2n+1} \left[\frac{n!}{(2n)!}\right]^2.$$

Hence

$$R_n = 2^{2n+1}\, \frac{(n!)^4}{[(2n!)]^3}\, \frac{f^{(2n)}(\xi)}{2n+1} \qquad (-1 \leqq \xi + 1).$$

The values of $\xi_k^{(n)}$ and $A_k^{(n)}$ were found already by GAUSS for the cases $n = 1, 2, 3, 4, 5, 6,$ and 7.

We give here (see table) these values for $n \leqq 5$ and refer the reader interested in the cases $n = 6$ and $n = 7$ to the monograph by A. A. MARKOFF [4].

n	$\xi_k^{(n)}$	$A_k^{(n)}$	$\log A_k^{(n)}$
1	0	2	0.3010300
2	-0.5773503	1	0
	$+0.5773503$	1	0
3	-0.7745967	$\frac{5}{9} = 0.5555556$	$\overline{1}.7447275$
	0	$\frac{8}{9} = 0.8888889$	$\overline{1}.9488475$
	$+0.7745967$	$\frac{5}{9} = 0.5555556$	$\overline{1}.7447275$
4	-0.8611363	0.3478548	$\overline{1}.5413981$
	-0.3399810	0.6521452	$\overline{1}.8143443$
	0.3399810	0.6521452	$\overline{1}.8143443$
	0.8611363	0.3478548	$\overline{1}.5413981$
5	-0.9061799	0.2369269	$\overline{1}.3746143$
	-0.5384693	0.4786287	$\overline{1}.6799987$
	0	0.5688889	$\overline{1}.7550275$
	0.5384693	0.4786287	$\overline{1}.6799987$
	0.9061799	0.2369269	$\overline{1}.3746143$

CHRISTOFFEL [1] found extremely simple expressions for the coefficients $A_k^{(n)}$ in GAUSS's formula. To derive these we apply the CHRISTOFFEL-DARBOUX formula (formula (93) of Volume II) to the LEGENDRE polynomials.

Since for these polynomials $\lambda_{n+1} = \dfrac{(n+1)^2}{(2n+1)(2n+3)}$, [13] the CHRISTOFFEL-DARBOUX formula reads (with $n-1$ instead of n):

$$\sum_{k=0}^{n-1} \hat{X}_k(t)\hat{X}_k(x) = \frac{n}{\sqrt{(2n-1)(2n+1)}} \frac{\hat{X}_n(t)\hat{X}_{n-1}(x) - \hat{X}_n(x)\hat{X}_{n-1}(t)}{t-x}.$$

Integrating this equation and recalling that $\hat{X}_0(t) = \dfrac{\sqrt{2}}{2}$, we obtain

$$1 = \frac{n}{\sqrt{(2n-1)(2n+1)}} \int_{-1}^{+1} \frac{\hat{X}_n(t)\hat{X}_{n-1}(x) - \hat{X}_n(x)\hat{X}_{n-1}(t)}{t-x} dt.$$

If in the place of the normalized polynomials $\hat{X}_n(x)$ we introduce the LEGENDRE polynomials

$$P_n(x) = \sqrt{\frac{2}{2n+1}}\, \hat{X}_n(x),$$

then the last equation assumes the form

$$\int_{-1}^{+1} \frac{P_n(t)P_{n-1}(x) - P_n(x)P_{n-1}(t)}{t-x} dt = \frac{2}{n}.$$

In this equation we now put $x = \xi_k^{(n)}$. Since $P_n(\xi_k^{(n)}) = 0$,

$$\int_{-1}^{+1} \frac{P_n(t)}{t - \xi_k^{(n)}} dt = \frac{2}{nP_{n-1}(\xi_k^{(n)})}.$$

In Chapter V of Volume II we proved at the end of § 2 that

$$(1-x^2)P_n'(x) = nP_{n-1}(x) - nxP_n(x),$$

and hence

$$nP_{n-1}(\xi_k^{(n)}) = [1 - (\xi_k^{(n)})^2]P_n'(\xi_k^{(n)});$$

this together with (215) gives finally

$$A_k^{(n)} = \frac{2}{1 - [\xi_k^{(n)}]^2} \frac{1}{[P_n'(\xi_k^{(n)})]^2}. \tag{216}$$

[13] Formula (125) in Volume II.

The use of GAUSS's formula is not restricted to the interval $[-1, +1]$; it can be applied to any other closed interval by a linear transformation.

II. The Hermite Formula

Suppose that $a = -1$, $b = +1$, $p(x) = \dfrac{1}{\sqrt{1 - x^2}}$. Hence the roots of the TCHEBYSHEFF polynomial $T_n(x)$ now serve as nodes, since the system of these polynomials is the orthogonal system with weight $\dfrac{1}{\sqrt{1 - x^2}}$. The roots of $T_n(x) = \cos(n \operatorname{arc\,cos} x)$ are

$$x_k = \cos \frac{2k - 1}{2n} \pi \qquad (k = 1, 2, \ldots, n),$$

and the coefficients A_k in the quadrature formula are given by

$$A_k = \int\limits_{-1}^{+1} \frac{T_n(x)}{T_n'(x_k)(x - x_k)} \frac{dx}{\sqrt{1 - x^2}}.$$

Setting $x = \cos \theta$ we have

$$A_k = \frac{1}{T_n'(x_k)} \int\limits_{0}^{\pi} \frac{\cos n\theta}{\cos \theta - \cos \theta_k} d\theta \quad \left(\theta_k = \frac{2k - 1}{2n} \pi \right).$$

Since $\dfrac{T_n(x)}{x - x_k}$ is an integral polynomial of degree $n - 1$,

$$\frac{\cos n\theta}{\cos \theta - \cos \theta_k}$$

is a polynomial of degree $n - 1$ in $\cos \theta$ and hence also an even trigonometric polynomial of order $n - 1$; therefore

$$\frac{\cos n\theta}{\cos \theta - \cos \theta_k} = B_0 + B_1 \cos \theta + \cdots + B_{n-1} \cos (n - 1)\theta. \qquad (217)$$

From this

$$\int\limits_{0}^{\pi} \frac{\cos n\theta \, d\theta}{\cos \theta - \cos \theta_k} = \pi B_0.$$

We have still to determine B_0. To this end we substitute

$$\theta = \theta_k, \quad \theta = \theta_k + \frac{2\pi}{n},$$

$$\theta = \theta_k + 2 \frac{2\pi}{n}, \quad \ldots, \quad \theta = \theta_k + (n - 1) \frac{2\pi}{n}$$

in succession into (217). Since

$$\left|\frac{\cos n\theta}{\cos \theta - \cos \theta_k}\right|_{\theta=\theta_k} = n\frac{\sin n\theta_k}{\sin \theta_k}$$

and [14]

$$\frac{\cos n\left(\theta_k + m\frac{2\pi}{n}\right)}{\cos \left(\theta_k + m\frac{2\pi}{n}\right) - \cos \theta_k} = 0 \quad (m = 1, 2, \ldots, n-1),$$

we obtain the n equations

$$B_0 + B_1 \cos \theta_k + B_2 \cos 2\theta_k + \cdots + B_{n-1} \cos (n-1)\theta_k = n\frac{\sin n\theta_k}{\sin \theta_k},$$

$$B_0 + B_1 \cos \left(\theta_k + \frac{2\pi}{n}\right) + B_2 \cos 2\left(\theta_k + \frac{2\pi}{n}\right)$$

$$+ \cdots + B_{n-1} \cos (n-1)\left(\theta_k + \frac{2\pi}{n}\right) = 0,$$

$$\cdot \quad \cdot \quad \cdot \quad \cdot \quad \cdot \quad \cdot \quad \cdot \quad \cdot \quad \cdot \quad \cdot \quad \cdot \quad \cdot \quad \cdot \quad \cdot \quad \cdot \quad \cdot \quad \cdot \quad \cdot \quad \cdot$$

$$B_0 + B_1 \cos \left(\theta_k + (n-1)\frac{2\pi}{n}\right) + B_2 \cos 2\left(\theta_k + (n-1)\frac{2\pi}{n}\right)$$

$$+ \cdots + B_{n-1} \cos (n-1)\left(\theta_k + (n-1)\frac{2\pi}{n}\right) = 0.$$

Adding these equations and noting that [15]

$$\sum_{r=0}^{n-1} \cos m\left(\theta_k + r\frac{2\pi}{n}\right) = 0,$$

---

[14] The numerator of this fraction is obviously zero, but the denominator is nonzero. For the equation $\cos \alpha = \cos \beta$ is possible only if either $\alpha - \beta = 2N\pi$ or $\alpha + \beta = 2N\pi$. Now $\left(\theta_k + m\frac{2\pi}{n}\right) - \theta_k \neq 2N\pi$, since $m = 1, 2, \ldots, n-1$. Also

$$2\theta_k + m\frac{2\pi}{n} = \frac{2k-1+2m}{n}\pi = 2N\pi,$$

since $2k - 1 + 2m \neq 2Nn$.

[15] If we multiply the sum

$$S = \sum_{r=0}^{n=1} \cos m\left(\theta_k + r\frac{2\pi}{n}\right)$$

by $2 \sin \frac{m\pi}{n} = 0$, we find with the help of the formula

$$2 \cos A \sin B = \sin (A+B) - \sin (A-B)$$

the identity

$$2S \sin \frac{m\pi}{n} = \sin m\left(\theta_k + \frac{2n-1}{n}\pi\right) - \sin m\left(\theta_k - \frac{\pi}{n}\right) = 0.$$

we find

$$B_0 = \frac{\sin n\theta_k}{\sin \theta_k};$$

hence

$$A_k = \frac{1}{T_n'(x_k)} \pi \frac{\sin n\theta_k}{\sin \theta_k}. \tag{218}$$

On the other hand $T_n(x) = \cos (n \text{ arc cos } x)$; hence

$$T_n'(x) = n \frac{\sin (n \text{ arc cos } x)}{\sqrt{1 - x^2}} = n \frac{\sin n\theta}{\sin \theta}$$

and in particular

$$T_n'(x_k) = n \frac{\sin n\theta_k}{\sin \theta_k}. \tag{219}$$

From (218) and (219) we obtain finally

$$A_k = \frac{\pi}{n},$$

a most remarkable result, for A_k is independent of k!

In our present case therefore the quadrature formula reads

$$\int_{-1}^{+1} \frac{f(x)}{\sqrt{1 - x^2}} dx = \frac{\pi}{n} \sum_{k=1}^{n} f\left(\cos \frac{2k - 1}{2n} \pi\right); \tag{220}$$

this is called the HERMITE *formula*.

According to the general theory, the remainder here is

$$R_n = \frac{f^{(2n)}(\xi)}{(2n)!} \int_{-1}^{+1} T_n^2(x) \frac{dx}{\sqrt{1 - x^2}} \qquad (-1 \leq \xi \leq +1).$$

But now $T_n(x) = \frac{1}{2^{n-1}} \cos (n \text{ arc cos } x)$, and hence

$$R_n = \frac{\pi}{(2n)! 2^{2n-1}} f^{(2n)}(\xi).$$

To make formula (220) useful for computing the integral

$$I = \int_a^b F(t)\, dt,$$

one first brings the integral I into the form

$$I = \int_{-1}^{+1} \varphi(x)\, dx$$

by the substitution $t = \dfrac{(b - a)x + a + b}{2}$ and then sets $f(x) = \varphi(x)\sqrt{1 - x^2}$.

I hereby becomes

$$I = \int\limits_{-1}^{+1} \frac{f(x)}{\sqrt{1 - x^2}}\, dx,$$

to which formula (220) may be applied.

III. If $a = -1$, $b = +1$, and $p(x) = \sqrt{1 - x^2}$, then the nodes are the roots of the TCHEBYSHEFF polynomials of second kind, i.e. the roots of the polynomials

$$U_n(x) = \frac{\sin\left[(n + 1)\, \text{arc}\, \cos x\right]}{\sqrt{1 - x^2}}.$$

The roots of $U_n(x)$ are

$$x_k = \cos \frac{k\pi}{n + 1} \qquad\qquad (k = 1, 2, \ldots, n).$$

The coefficients A_k are then

$$A_k = \int\limits_{-1}^{+1} \frac{U_n(x)}{U_n'(x_k)(x - x_k)} \sqrt{1 - x^2}\, dx$$

$$= \frac{1}{U_n'(x_k)} \int\limits_{0}^{\pi} \frac{\sin(n + 1)\theta}{\cos\theta - \cos\theta_k} \sin\theta\, d\theta,$$

where $\theta_k = \dfrac{k\pi}{n + 1}$. Now

$$\sin(n + 1)\theta \sin\theta = \frac{1}{2}\left[\cos n\theta - \cos(n + 2)\theta\right].$$

Recalling moreover that [16] $\cos(n + 2)\theta_k = \cos n\theta_k$, we obtain

$$A_k = \frac{1}{2U_n'(x_k)}\left\{ \int\limits_{0}^{\pi} \frac{\cos n\theta - \cos n\theta_k}{\cos\theta - \cos\theta_k}\, d\theta \right.$$

$$\left. - \int\limits_{0}^{\pi} \frac{\cos(n + 2)\theta - \cos(n + 2)\theta_k}{\cos\theta - \cos\theta_k}\, d\theta \right\}$$

---

[16] This follows from the fact that $(n + 2)\theta_k + n\theta_k = 2k\pi$.

The polynomial $T_n(x) - T_k(x_k)$ is divisible by $x - x_k$ without remainder. Hence

$$\frac{\cos n\theta - \cos n\theta_k}{\cos \theta - \cos \theta_k}$$

is an even trigonometric polynomial of order $n - 1$:

$$\frac{\cos n\theta - \cos n\theta_k}{\cos \theta - \cos \theta_k} = B_0 + B_1 \cos \theta + \cdots + B_{n-1} \cos (n - 1)\theta,$$

whence

$$\int_0^\pi \frac{\cos n\theta - \cos n\theta_k}{\cos \theta - \cos \theta_k} \, d\theta = \pi B_0.$$

As in the preceding example we again obtain

$$B_0 = \frac{\sin n\theta_k}{\sin \theta_k},$$

where the method of computing B_0 is entirely analogous to the above method.
Similarly one obtain

$$\int_0^\pi \frac{\cos (n + 2)\theta - \cos (n + 2)\theta_k}{\cos \theta - \cos \theta_k} \, d\theta = \pi \frac{\sin (n + 2)\theta_k}{\sin \theta_k}.$$

Hence

$$A_k = \frac{\pi}{2U_n'(x_k)} \cdot \frac{\sin n\theta_k - \sin (n + 2)\theta_k}{\sin \theta_k}$$

$$= -\frac{\pi}{U_n'(x_k)} \cos (n + 1)\theta_k = \frac{(-1)^{k+1}\pi}{U_n'(x_k)}.$$

Now

$$U_n(x) = \frac{-(n + 1) \cos [(n + 1) \arccos x] + \sin [(n + 1) \arccos x] \dfrac{x}{\sqrt{1 - x^2}}}{1 - x^2},$$

and hence

$$U_n'(x_k) = \frac{-(n + 1) \cos (n + 1)\theta_k}{\sin^2 \theta_k} = (-1)^{k+1} \frac{n + 1}{\sin^2 \theta_k};$$

from this it follows finally that

$$A_k = \frac{\pi}{n + 1} \sin^2 \theta_k,$$

so that the quadrature formula reads

$$\int\limits_{-1}^{+1} \sqrt{1 - x^2}\, f(x)\, dx = \frac{\pi}{n + 1} \sum_{k=1}^{n} \sin^2 \frac{k\pi}{n + 1} f\left(\cos \frac{k\pi}{n + 1}\right).$$

The remainder for this formula is

$$R_n = \frac{f^{(2n)}(\xi)}{(2n)!} \int\limits_{-1}^{+1} \sqrt{1 - x^2}\, U_n^2(x)\, dx.$$

Now $\tilde{U}_n(x) = \dfrac{1}{2^n} \dfrac{\sin (n + 1)\, \text{arc cos } x}{\sqrt{1 - x^2}}$, whence it follows that

$$R_n = \frac{\pi}{(2n)!\, 2^{2n+1}} f^{(2n)}(\xi) \qquad\qquad (-1 \leqq \xi \leqq 1)$$

IV. Without going into the details, which are quite similar to the preceding, we add that for $a = -1$, $b = +1$, and

$$p(x) = \sqrt{\frac{1 - x}{1 + x}}$$

we obtain the quadrature formula

$$\int\limits_{-1}^{+1} \sqrt{\frac{1 - x}{1 + x}}\, f(x)\, dx = \frac{4\pi}{2n + 1} \sum_{k=1}^{n} \sin^2 \frac{k\pi}{2n + 1} f\left(\cos \frac{2k\pi}{2n + 1)}\right),$$

with remainder

$$R_n = \frac{\pi}{(2n)!\, 2^{2n}} f^{(2n)}(\xi) \qquad\qquad (-1 \leqq \xi \leqq +1).$$

CHAPTER VI

SUPPLEMENT TO THE THEORY
OF APPROXIMATION QUADRATURES

§1. The General Quadrature Process and Its Convergence

We obtained the formula

$$\int_a^b f(x)\,dx = \sum_{k=1}^n A_k f(x_k) \tag{221}$$

by integrating the approximation $f(x) \approx L(x)$, where $L(x)$ was a LAGRANGE interpolation polynomial for the function $f(x)$. However, one need not start with an interpolation polynomial in order to arrive at such an approximation formula. On the contrary, every approximation to the function $f(x)$ by means of a summation formula

$$f(x) \approx \sum_{k=1}^n f(x_k)\varphi_k(x)$$

leads after integration to an approximation equation of the form (221). If, for example, we take the BERNSTEIN polynomials

$$\sum_{k=0}^n f\left(\frac{k}{n}\right) C_n^k x^k (1-x)^{n-k},$$

we obtain the quadrature formula

$$\int_0^1 f(x)\,dx = \sum_{k=0}^n A_k f\left(\frac{k}{n}\right).$$

Here

$$A_k = C_n^k \int_0^1 x^k (1-x)^{n-k}\,dx = C_n^k B(k+1, n-k+1)$$

$$= C_n^k \frac{\Gamma(k+1)\Gamma(n-k+1)}{\Gamma(n+2)} = \frac{1}{n+1}.$$

We may consider the type of formula (221) from still a more general point of view by dropping the inquiry as to the origin of the coefficients A_k. Of course, we may no longer assert—as we have formerly done when formula (221) was derived from an interpolation polynomial—that the formula becomes an exact equation for every polynomial of H_{n-1}.

These considerations lead naturally to the formulation of the following problem. Given two triangular matrices—a matrix of nodes and a matrix of coefficients—

$$
\left.
\begin{array}{l}
x_1^{(1)}, \qquad\qquad\qquad\quad A_1^{(1)}, \\[2mm]
x_1^{(2)},\ x_2^{(2)}, \qquad\qquad\quad A_1^{(2)},\ A_2^{(2)}, \\[2mm]
\cdots\cdots\cdots\cdots\cdots\cdots\cdots\cdots\cdots \\[2mm]
x_1^{(n)},\ x_2^{(n)},\ \ldots,\ x_n^{(n)} \quad A_1^{(n)},\ A_2^{(n)},\ \ldots,\ A_n^{(n)}, \\[2mm]
\cdots\cdots\cdots\cdots\cdots\cdots\cdots\cdots\cdots
\end{array}
\right\}
\qquad (222)
$$

where all nodes belong to a particular interval $[a, b]$, the functional

$$
Q_n(f) = \sum_{k=1}^{n} A_k^{(n)} f(x_k^{(n)})
\qquad (223)
$$

may be applied to every function defined on $[a, b]$. The question is now: under what conditions is it the case that

$$
\lim_{n \to \infty} Q_n(f) = \int_a^b f(x)\, dx?
\qquad (224)
$$

If (224) is satisfied, then we say that the *quadrature process* generated by the matrices (222) *converges* for the function $f(x)$.

Theorem 1. *The quadrature process generated by the matrices (222) converges for every continuous function $f(x)$ defined on $[a, b]$ if and only if*

1. *the process converges for every polynomial, and*
2. *there exists a constant K such that*

$$
\sum_{k=1}^{n} |A_k^{(n)}| \leq K \qquad (k = 1, 2, \ldots, n). \quad (225)
$$

Proof. We first prove sufficiency.[1] Suppose the conditions are satisfied and let $f(x) \in C([a, b])$. Given $\varepsilon > 0$, we can find a polynomial $P(x)$ which for all $x \in [a, b]$ satisfies the inequality

$$
|P(x) - f(x)| < \varepsilon.
$$

---

[1] That the conditions are sufficient was first proved by V. A. STEKLOV [2]; necessity was first proved by G. POLYA [1].

Then

$$|Q_n(P) - Q_n(f)| = \left| \sum_{k=1}^{n} A_k^{(n)}[P(x_k^{(n)}) - f(x_k^{(n)})] \right| \leqq \varepsilon \sum_{k=1}^{n} |A_k^{(n)}| \leqq K\varepsilon,$$

whereupon the inequality

$$\left| \int_a^b f(x)\, dx - Q_n(f) \right| \leqq \left| \int_a^b f(x)\, dx - \int_a^b P(x)\, dx \right|$$

$$+ \left| \int_a^b P(x)\, dx - Q_n(P) \right| + |Q_n(P) - Q_n(f)|$$

affords the proof that

$$\left| \int_a^b f(x)\, dx - Q_n(f) \right| \leqq \varepsilon[b - a + K] + \left| \int_a^b P(x)\, dx - Q_n(P) \right|.$$

But since $P(x)$ is a polynomial, for sufficiently large n

$$\left| \int_a^b P(x)\, dx - Q_n(P) \right| < \varepsilon;$$

for this n therefore

$$\left| \int_a^b f(x)\, dx - Q_n(f) \right| < \varepsilon[b - a + K + 1],$$

from which (224) follows immediately.

We must prove necessity only for condition 2; the proof for condition 1 is trivial. The proof will again proceed by the indirect "sliding hump" method; we hence assume that the quadrature process converges for every continuous function without condition 2 being satisfied. We now construct a continuous function $\varphi_n(x)$ on $[a, b]$ which satisfies the conditions

$$|\varphi_n(x)| \leqq 1, \ \varphi_n(x_k^{(n)}) = \text{sign } A_k^{(n)} \quad (k = 1, 2, \ldots, n).$$

The function is hereby already defined at the nodes $x_k^{(n)}$; at the other points we define it by requiring that it be linear between two adjacent nodes, but that on the intervals $[a, x_1^{(n)}]$ and $[x_n^{(n)}, b]$—in the event that these occur—it be constant. It is easily seen that

$$Q_n(\varphi_n) = \sum_{k=1}^{n} A_k^{(n)} \varphi_n(x_k^{(n)}) = \sum_{k=1}^{n} |A_k^{(n)}|.$$

For simplicity we set

$$\sum_{k=1}^{n} |A_k^{(n)}| = L_n, \tag{226}$$

whereby

$$Q_n(\varphi_n) = L_n.$$

After we have thus constructed the functions $\varphi_n(x)$ for every n, we set $n_1 = 1$. Since for the (continuous!) function $\varphi_{n_1}(x)$ the quadrature process converges,

$$\lim_{n \to \infty} Q_n(\varphi_{n_1}) = \int_a^b \varphi_{n_1}(x)\, dx.$$

But since $|\varphi_{n_1}(x)| \leqq 1$,

$$\left| \int_a^b \varphi_{n_1}(x)\, dx \right| \leqq b - a;$$

there therefore exists a number N_1 such that for $n > N_1$

$$|Q_n(\varphi_{n_1})| < e(b - a).$$

Since on the other hand the second condition is not satisfied, there exists an index $n_2 > N_1$ such that

$$L_{n_2} > 2 \cdot 2!.$$

The function

$$\frac{\varphi_{n_1}(x)}{1!} + \frac{\varphi_{n_2}(x)}{2!}$$

is continuous, so that the quadrature process for it converges and

$$\left| \int_a^b \left[\frac{\varphi_{n_1}(x)}{1!} + \frac{\varphi_{n_2}(x)}{2!} \right] dx \right| \leqq \left(\frac{1}{1!} + \frac{1}{2!} \right) (b - a) < (e - 1)(b - a).$$

There therefore exists a number N_2 such that for $n > N_2$ the inequality

$$\left| Q_n \left[\frac{\varphi_{n_1}(x)}{1!} + \frac{\varphi_{n_2}(x)}{2!} \right] \right| < e(b - a)$$

holds.

Since now condition 2 is not satisfied, it follows that there exists an index $n_3 > N_2$ such that

$$L_{n_3} > 3 \cdot 3!.$$

We now assume that the indices $n_1, n_2, \ldots, n_{m-1}$ have already been determined. The function

$$\sum_{i=1}^{m-1} \frac{\varphi_{ni}(x)}{i!}$$

is then continuous, so that the quadrature process for it converges. But now

$$\left| \sum_{i=1}^{m-1} \frac{\varphi_{ni}(x)}{i!} \right| < \sum_{i=1}^{\infty} \frac{1}{i!} = e - 1.$$

Therefore

$$\left| \int_{n}^{b} \left[\sum_{i=1}^{m-1} \frac{\varphi_{ni}(x)}{i!} \right] dx \right| \leqq (e - 1)(b - a),$$

so that there exists a number N_{m-1} such that for $n > N_{m-1}$ the inequality

$$\left| Q_n \left[\sum_{i=1}^{m-1} \frac{\varphi_{ni}(x)}{i!} \right] \right| < e(b - a)$$

holds. Since condition 2 is not fulfilled, there exists an index $n_m > N_{m-1}$ such that

$$L_{n_m} > m \cdot m!. \tag{227}$$

In this manner we obtain an infinite sequence of indices $n_1, n_2, n_3, \ldots$. If we now set

$$f(x) = \sum_{i=1}^{\infty} \frac{\varphi_{ni}(x)}{i!},$$

$f(x)$ is obviously a continuous function for which, contrary to assumption, the quadrature process diverges. Indeed, if $m > 1$ is a natural number

$$f(x) = \sum_{i=1}^{m-1} \frac{\varphi_{ni}(x)}{i!} + \frac{\varphi_{nm}(x)}{m!} + \sum_{i=m+1}^{\infty} \frac{\varphi_{ni}(x)}{i!}$$

and

$$Q_{n_m}(f) = Q_{n_m} \left(\sum_{i=1}^{m-1} \frac{\varphi_{ni}(x)}{i!} \right) + \frac{1}{m!} L_{nm} + Q_{nm} \left(\sum_{i=m+1}^{\infty} \frac{\varphi_{ni}(x)}{i!} \right). \tag{228}$$

Since now $n_m > N_{m-1}$,

$$\left| Q_{nm}\left(\sum_{i=1}^{m-1}\frac{\varphi_{ni}(x)}{i!}\right) \right| < e(b-a). \tag{229}$$

The function

$$\rho(x) = \sum_{i=m+1}^{\infty}\frac{\varphi_{ni}(x)}{i!}$$

admits the estimate

$$|\rho(x)| \leqq \sum_{i=m+1}^{\infty}\frac{1}{i!} = \frac{1}{(m+1)!}\left[1 + \frac{1}{m+2} + \frac{1}{(m+2)(m+3)} + \cdots\right].$$

But now

$$1 + \frac{1}{m+2} + \frac{1}{(m+2)(m+3)} + \cdots < 1 + \frac{1}{m+2} + \frac{1}{(m+2)^2}$$

$$+ \cdots = \frac{m+2}{m+1} < \frac{m+1}{m},$$

and hence

$$|\rho(x)| < \frac{1}{m \cdot m!}.$$

Thus

$$|Q_{n_m}(\rho)| = \left| \sum_{k=1}^{n_m} A_k^{(n_m)}\rho(x_k^{(n_m)}) \right| \leqq \frac{L_{n_m}}{m \cdot m!}. \tag{230}$$

From (228), (229), and (230) we obtain

$$Q_{nm}(f) > \frac{1}{m!}L_{nm} - e(b-a) - \frac{1}{m \cdot m!}L_{nm},$$

and from this according to (227)

$$Q_{n_m}(f) > m - 1 - e(b-a).$$

But this means that

$$\lim_{m\to\infty} Q_{n_m}(f) = +\infty,$$

so that the quadrature process for $f(x)$ diverges. The theorem is herewith completely proved.

As is evident from formula (223), the functional $Q_n(f)$ depends on the $2n$ parameters $x_1^{(n)}, x_2^{(n)}, \ldots, x_n^{(n)}$ and $A_1^{(n)}, A_2^{(n)}, \ldots, A_n^{(n)}$. These parameters are in general independent, but every condition which we impose reduces the number of free parameters. For example, GAUSS's condition that the quadrature formula should be exact for every polynomial in H_{2n-1} actually consists of $2n$ conditions and defines therefore the nodes as well as the coefficients uniquely.

If the two matrices (222) are related by

$$A_k^{(n)} = \int_a^b l_k^{(n)}(x)\,dx, \tag{231}$$

where

$$l_k^{(n)}(x) = \frac{\omega_n(x)}{\omega_n'(x_k^{(n)})(x - x_k^{(n)})}, \quad \omega_n(x) = \prod_{k=1}^{n}(x - x_k^{(n)}),$$

then this interpolation process is called an *interpolation quadrature*. In such a process the nodes are arbitrary, but after the nodes are chosen the coefficients are uniquely determined.

Theorem 2. *A quadrature method is an interpolation quadrature if and only if the equation*

$$Q_n(f) = \int_a^b f(x)\,dx \tag{232}$$

is exact for every polynomial in H_{n-1}.

Proof. Suppose that (231) is satisfied. If $f(x) \in H_{n-1}$, then $f(x)$ is identical with its LAGRANGE interpolation polynomial over the nodes $x_k^{(n)}$:

$$f(x) = \sum_{k=1}^{n} f(x_k^{(n)}) l_i^{(n)}(x).$$

Integrating this equation we obtain, on the basis of (231), the equation (232). If, conversely, (232) holds for every polynomial in H_{n-1}, then in particular it holds for $l_i^{(n)}$:

$$\sum_{k=1}^{n} A_k^{(n)} l_i^{(n)}(x_k^{(n)}) = \int_a^b l_k^{(n)}(x)\,dx. \tag{233}$$

But now $l_i^{(n)}(x_i^{(n)}) = 1$ and $l_i^{(n)}(x_{k \neq i}^{(n)}) = 0$. Equation (233) therefore implies (231).

An interpolation quadrature obviously converges for every polynomial; indeed, if $f(x)$ is a polynomial of degree m, then (232) is satisfied for $n > m$. We therefore have

Theorem 3. *An interpolation quadrature converges for every continuous function if and only if*

$$\sum_{k=1}^{n} |A_k^{(n)}| \leqq K, \tag{234}$$

where K is a constant which does not depend on n.

In conclusion we present a necessary condition for the convergence of a quadrature process:

Theorem 4 (V. A. STEKLOV [2]). *If a quadrature process converges for every continuous function, then to every interval $[p, q] \subset [a, b]$ there corresponds a number N such that for every $n > N$ the interval $[p, q]$ contains at least one node $x_k^{(n)}$.*

Proof. Assume that for some interval $[p, q] \subset [a, b]$ the condition is not satisfied. There then exists an infinite sequence of indices $n_1 < n_2 < n_3 < \cdots$ such that none of the nodes $x_k^{(n_i)}$ $(k = 1, 2, \ldots, n_i)$ lies in $[p, q]$.

Now let $h = \dfrac{q - p}{3}$, and define a function $\psi(x)$ as follows: [2]

$$\psi(x) = \begin{cases} 0 & \text{for } a \leqq x \leqq p \text{ and } q \leqq x \leqq b, \\ 1 & \text{for } p + h \leqq x \leqq q - h, \\ \text{linear} & \text{for } p \leqq x \leqq p + h \text{ and } q - h \leqq x \leqq q. \end{cases}$$

Since $\psi(x)$ continuous,

$$\lim_{n \to \infty} Q_n(\psi) = \int_a^b \psi(x)\, dx.$$

However, this leads to a contradiction. Since $x_k^{(n_i)} \notin [p, q]$, $\psi(x_k^{(n_i)}) = 0$; therefore

$$Q_{n_i}(\psi) = \sum_{k=1}^{n_i} A_k^{(n_i)} \psi(x_k^{(n_i)}) = 0.$$

On the other hand, $\psi(x)$ is non-negative, and

$$\int_a^b \psi(x)\, dx > \int_{p+h}^{q-h} \psi(x)\, dx = h > 0.$$

The theorem is herewith proved.

[2] The reader should sketch the graph of the function $\psi(x)$.

§2. Quadratures with Positive Coefficients

We shall now consider quadrature processes in which all the coefficients $A_k^{(n)}$ are non-negative; these processes have a number of special properties.

Theorem 1 (V. A. STEKLOV [2]). *If all coefficients $A_k^{(n)}$ are non-negative, then the quadrature process converges for every continuous function if and only if it converges for every polynomial.*

Proof. The necessity of the condition is trivial; that it is also sufficient we prove with the help of the polynomial $f(x) \equiv 1$. For this polynomial by hypothesis

$$\lim_{n \to \infty} Q_n(1) = \int_a^b dx = b - a.$$

The numbers $Q_n(1)$ are therefore bounded. On the other hand,

$$Q_n(1) = \sum_{k=1}^n A_k^{(n)} = \sum_{k=1}^n |A_k^{(n)}|,$$

so that the second condition of Theorem 1, § 1 is also satisfied; this theorem now guarantees the convergence of the process for every continuous function.

Corollary. *An interpolation quadrature with non-negative coefficients converges for every continuous function.*

This follows from the fact already established that an interpolation quadrature converges for every polynomial.

An example of an interpolation quadrature with non-negative coefficients $A_k^{(n)}$ is the GAUSS method in which $a = -1$, $b = +1$, and the nodes $x_k^{(n)}$ are roots of a LEGENDRE polynomial. This was proved in the lemma of § 3, Chapter V.

We shall now present several other interpolation quadratures with non-negative coefficients.

Theorem 2. *If $a = -1$, $b = +1$, and the nodes $x_k^{(n)}$ are the roots of the* TCHEBYSHEFF *polynomial $T_n(x)$, then the coefficients $A_k^{(n)}$ are positive.*[3]

Remark. This theorem is not covered by Lemma 3, § 3, Chapter V. This lemma states that the coefficients

$$\int_{-1}^{+1} \frac{T_n(x)}{T_n'(x_k^{(n)})(x - x_k^{(n)})} \frac{dx}{\sqrt{1 - x^2}}$$

[3] FEJÉR [5].

are positive, while it is here a question of the coefficients

$$A_k^{(n)} = \int_{-1}^{+1} \frac{T_n(x)}{T_n'(x_k^{(n)})(x - x_k^{(n)})} \, dx. \qquad (235)$$

Proof. We substitute $x = \cos\theta$ into (235). Noting that

$$T_n'(x_k^{(n)}) = \frac{(-1)^{k-1}}{\sin\theta_k} n \qquad \left(\theta_k = \frac{2k-1}{2n}\pi\right),$$

we obtain

$$A_k^{(n)} = (-1)^{k-1} \frac{\sin\theta_k}{n} \int_0^\pi \frac{\cos n\theta}{\cos\theta - \cos\theta_k} \sin\theta \, d\theta. \qquad (236)$$

If we put

$$\varphi_k(\theta) = \sum_{r=1}^{n-1} \cos r\theta \cos r\theta_k,$$

then an elementary trigonometric identity gives

$$2\varphi_k(\theta) = \sum_{r=1}^{n-1} [\cos r(\theta + \theta_k) + \cos r(\theta - \theta_k)].$$

From this it follows (using the same trigonometric identity) that

$$4\varphi_k(\theta)\cos\theta = \sum_{r=1}^{n-1} \{\cos[(r+1)\theta + r\theta_k] + \cos[(r-1)\theta + r\theta_k]$$
$$+ \cos[(r+1)\theta - r\theta_k] + \cos[(r-1)\theta - r\theta_k]\}$$

and similarly

$$4\varphi_k(\theta)\cos\theta_k = \sum_{r=1}^{n-1} \{\cos[r\theta + (r+1)\theta_k] + \cos[r\theta + (r-1)\theta_k]$$
$$+ \cos[r\theta - (r-1)\theta_k] + \cos[r\theta - (r+1)\theta_k]\}.$$

Subtracting the last equation from the preceding one we obtain

$$4\varphi_k(\theta)(\cos\theta - \cos\theta_k) = \cos[n\theta + (n-1)\theta_k]$$
$$- \cos[(n-1)\theta + n\theta_k] + \cos[n\theta - (n-1)\theta_k]$$
$$- \cos[(n-1)\theta - n\theta_k] - 2(\cos\theta - \cos\theta_k). \qquad (237)$$

Now

$$\cos[n\theta + (n-1)\theta_k] + \cos[n\theta - (n-1)\theta_k] = 2\cos n\theta \cos(n-1)\theta_k$$
$$\cos[(n-1)\theta + n\theta_k] + \cos[(n-1)\theta - n\theta_k] = 2\cos(n-1)\theta \cos n\theta_k.$$

Noting that

$$\cos n\theta_k = 0, \quad \cos (n-1)\theta_k = \sin n\theta_k \sin \theta_k = (-1)^{k-1} \sin \theta_k,$$

we can rearrange equation (237) to obtain

$$2\varphi_k(\theta)(\cos \theta - \cos \theta_k) = (-1)^{k-1} \sin \theta_k \cos n\theta - (\cos \theta - \cos \theta_k);$$

whence

$$(-1)^{k-1} \frac{\cos n\theta}{\cos \theta - \cos \theta_k} \sin \theta_k = 1 + 2\varphi_k(\theta).$$

Equation (236) thus becomes

$$A_k^{(n)} = \frac{1}{n} \int_0^\pi \left[1 + 2 \sum_{r=1}^{n-1} \cos r\theta \cos r\theta_k \right] \sin \theta \, d\theta.$$

Now

$$2 \int_0^\pi \cos r\theta \sin \theta \, d\theta = \int_0^\pi [\sin (r+1)\theta - \sin (r-1)\theta] \, d\theta.$$

If r is odd the integral on the righthand side is zero. If r is even this integral has the value

$$-\left(\frac{2}{r-1} - \frac{2}{r+1} \right),$$

and therefore

$$A_k^{(n)} = \frac{2}{n} \left\{ 1 - \left(1 - \frac{1}{3}\right) \cos 2\theta_k - \left(\frac{1}{3} - \frac{1}{5}\right) \cos 4\theta_k - \cdots \right.$$
$$\left. - \left(\frac{1}{m-1} - \frac{1}{m+1}\right) \cos m\theta_k \right\},$$

where $m = n-1$ if n is odd and $m = n-2$ if n is even. Hence

$$A_k^{(n)} > \frac{2}{n} \left\{ 1 - \left(1 - \frac{1}{3}\right) - \left(\frac{1}{3} - \frac{1}{5}\right) - \cdots \right.$$
$$\left. - \left(\frac{1}{m-1} - \frac{1}{m+1}\right) \right\} = \frac{2}{n(m+1)}$$

and *a fortiori* $A_k^{(n)} > 0$. The theorem is herewith proved.

Quite similarly one proves

Theorem 3. *If $a = -1$, $b = +1$, and the nodes are roots of the* TCHEBY-SHEFF *polynomial of second kind*

$$U_n(x) = \frac{\sin(n+1)\arccos x}{\sqrt{1-x^2}},$$

then the coefficients $A_k^{(n)}$ are positive.[4]

We shall not stop to prove this theorem here.

Theorem 4. *If a quadrature process with non-negative coefficients [5] converges for every continuous function and if*

$$B_n = \max A_k^{(n)} \qquad\qquad (k = 1, 2, \ldots, n),$$

then

$$\lim_{n \to \infty} B_n = 0.$$

Proof. We prove the theorem indirectly. If B_n does not converge to zero, then it is possible to find a number $\sigma > 0$ and an infinite sequence of indices $\{n_i\}$ such that

$$B_{n_i} > \sigma.$$

Let $k(i)$ be such that $A_{k(i)}^{(n_i)} = B_{n_i}$. The points $x_{k(i)}^{(n_i)}$ have a limit point ξ in $[a, b]$. We assume that $a < \xi < b$ (if $\xi = a$ or $\xi = b$ the change in the proof is minor).

We now introduce a number $\delta > 0$, the choice of which we subsequently specify more precisely; for the time being it is required to satisfy the conditions

$$\delta < \frac{\xi - a}{2}, \qquad \delta < \frac{b - \xi}{2}.$$

---

[4] FEJÉR [5]. Theorems 2 and 3 were generalized by SZEGÖ [1] who proved (loc. cit., p. 350) that $A_k^{(n)} > 0$ if the nodes $x^{(n)}$ are roots of an ultraspherical JACOBI polynomial $J^{(\alpha,\alpha)}(x)$ and $-1 < \alpha \leqq 0$ or $\frac{1}{2} \leqq \alpha \leqq 1$. If $-1 < \alpha \leqq \frac{3}{2}$, then $A_k^{(n)} > 0$ at least for all sufficient large n.

[5] The condition $A_k^{(n)} > 0$ is essential. Thus, for example, the process

$$Q_n(f) = \frac{1}{n} \sum_{k=1}^{n} f\left(\frac{k}{n}\right) + f(1) - f\left(\frac{n-1}{n}\right)$$

converges for every function $f(x) \in C([0, 1])$, yet

$$\max |A_k^{(n)}| > 1.$$

We define a function $\psi(x)$ as follows: [6]

$$\psi(x) = \begin{cases} 0 & \text{for } a \le x \le \xi - 2\delta \text{ and } \xi + 2\delta \le x \le b, \\ 1 & \text{for } \xi - \delta \le x \le \xi + \delta, \\ \text{linear} & \text{for } \xi - 2\delta \le x \le \xi - \delta, \ \xi + \delta \le x \le \xi + 2\delta. \end{cases}$$

Since $\psi(x)$ is continuous, we have

$$\lim_{n \to \infty} Q_n(\psi) = \int\limits_a^b \psi(x)\, dx. \qquad (238)$$

Since however $\psi(x) \le 1$,

$$\int\limits_a^b \psi(x)\, dx = \int\limits_{\xi-2\delta}^{\xi+2\delta} \psi(x)\, dx \le 4\delta.$$

On the other hand it is possible to find values of i sufficiently large that $x_{k(i)}^{(ni)} \in [\xi - \delta,\ \xi + \delta]$; for these i

$$Q_n(\psi) = \sum_{k=1}^{ni} A_k^{(ni)} \psi(x_k^{(ni)}) \ge A_{k(i)}^{(ni)} > \sigma.$$

If we now choose δ such that $4\delta < \sigma$, then equation (238) becomes impossible. This completes the proof of the theorem.

§3. A Theorem due to R. O. Kusmin

The preceding investigations show that those interpolation quadratures are to be considered "good" for which

$$\sum_{k=1}^{n} |A_k^{(n)}| \le K, \qquad (239)$$

since these converge for every continuous function. We further saw that one obtains such good processes by choosing the roots of the Legendre or Tchebysheff polynomials as nodes; we still lack an example in which (239) is not satisfied. One might possibly think that all interpolation quadratures satisfy condition (239). That this is not so is shown by the following theorem which says in effect that equidistant nodes yield "bad" interpolation quadratures. But this is not actually very surprising: as we established in Chapter II, the interpolation process itself is extremely bad with equidistant nodes; this is reflected by the rapid increase of λ_n.

[6] The reader should sketch the curve.

Theorem (R. O. Kusmin [1]).   *If the nodes of an interpolation quadrature over $[-1, +1]$ are chosen to be equidistant (with $x_1 = -1$ and $x_n = +1$), then the condition*

$$\sum_{k=1}^{n} |A_k^{(n)}| \leqq \cdot K$$

is not satisfied.

Actually Kusmin proved still more than is stated in the theorem; he established asymptotic formulas for all the coefficients $A_k^{(n)}$ and proved that all these coefficients themselves become arbitrarily large (in absolute value) with increasing n. We shall here be content with the proof of the above theorem with which R. O. Kusmin has himself generously provided me; this proof is considerably simpler than the derivation of the asymptotic formulas just mentioned.

Proof.   We consider the nodes

$$x_k = -1 + \frac{k-1}{n} \qquad (k = 1, 2, \ldots, 2n + 1). \quad (240)$$

The coefficient A_{n+1} then has the form

$$A_{n+1} = \int_{-1}^{+1} \frac{(x - x_1) \cdots (x - x_n)(x - x_{n+2}) \cdots (x - x_{2n+1})}{(x_{n+1} - x_1) \cdots (x_{n+1} - x_n)(x_{n+1} - x_{n+2}) \cdots (x_{n+1} - x_{2n+1})} \, dx;$$

hence

$$A_{n+1} = \int_{-1}^{+1} \frac{(x + 1)\left(x + 1 - \frac{1}{n}\right) \cdots \left(x + \frac{1}{n}\right)\left(x - \frac{1}{n}\right) \cdots (x - 1)}{\dfrac{n}{n}\dfrac{n-1}{n} \cdots \dfrac{1}{n}\dfrac{-1}{n}\dfrac{-2}{n} \cdots \dfrac{-n}{n}} \, dx,$$

and from this

$$A_{n+1} = \frac{(-1)^n n^{2n}}{(n!)^2} \int_{-1}^{+1} (x + 1) \cdots \left(x + \frac{1}{n}\right)\left(x - \frac{1}{n}\right) \cdots (x - 1) \, dx.$$

By means of the substitution $nx = t$ we obtain

$$A_{n+1} = \frac{(-1)^n}{n(n!)^2} \int_{-n}^{n} (t + n) \cdots (t + 1)(t - 1) \cdots (t - n) \, dt.$$

Since the integrand is an even function, it follows that

$$A_{n+1} = \frac{(-1)^n 2}{n(n!)^2} \int_0^n (t+n)\cdots(t+1)(t-1)\cdots(t-n)\, dt. \quad (241)$$

If we now split off the integral

$$\alpha_n = \frac{(-1)^n 2}{n(n!)^2} \int_0^1 (t+n)\cdots(t+1)(t-1)\cdots(t-n)\, dt,$$

then it is evident that

$$\alpha_n = \frac{2}{n} \int_0^1 \left(1 - \frac{t^2}{1^2}\right)\left(1 - \frac{t^2}{2^2}\right)\cdots\left(1 - \frac{t^2}{n^2}\right) dt.$$

The integrand is here positive and no greater than one. Hence $0 < \alpha_n < \frac{2}{n}$, and therefore

$$\lim_{n \to \infty} \alpha_n = 0. \quad (242)$$

In the integral

$$\int_1^n (t+n)\cdots(t+1)(t-1)\cdots(t-n)\, dt$$

we substitute $t = n - z$. This gives

$$A_{n+1} = \alpha_n + \frac{(-1)^n 2}{n(n!)^2} \int_0^{n-1} (2n - z)\cdots(n+1-z)$$
$$(-1 - z)\ldots(1 - z)(-z)\, dz$$

and from this

$$A_{n+1} = \alpha_n + \frac{(-1)^{n+1} 2}{n(n!)^2} \int_0^{n-1} \psi(z)\frac{z\, dz}{n - z}, \quad (243)$$

where for brevity we have put

$$\psi(z) = (2n - z)(2n - 1 - z)\cdots(1 - z). \quad (244)$$

If we now decompose the integral

$$I = \int_0^{n-1} \psi(z)\frac{z\, dz}{n - z}$$

into summands according to the scheme

$$\int\limits_0^{n-1} = \int\limits_0^1 + \int\limits_1^2 + \int\limits_2^3 + \int\limits_3^4 + \int\limits_4^5 + \int\limits_5^{n-1}, \tag{245}$$

and denote these summands by I_0, I_1, I_2, I_3, I_4, I^* respectively, then it will be shown that I_0 is the principal component and that all the others become arbitrarily small *with respect to* I_0.

The integral I_0 has the form

$$I_0 = \int\limits_0^1 [(2n - z)(2n - 1 - z)\cdots(2 - z)] \frac{(1 - z)z}{n - z}\, dz.$$

For $0 < z \leqq 1$ the expression in the brackets is not less than $(2n - 1)!$ Therefore

$$I_0 > (2n - 1)! \int\limits_0^1 \frac{(1 - z)z}{n - z}\, dz,$$

and since

$$\int\limits_0^1 \frac{(1 - z)z}{n - z}\, dz > \frac{1}{n} \int\limits_0^1 (1 - z)z\, dz = \frac{1}{6n},$$

it follows that

$$I_0 > \frac{(2n - 1)!}{6n}. \tag{246}$$

We now show that each of the integrals I_0, I_1, I_2, I_3, I_4 (with the exception of I_0 itself) becomes arbitrarily small with respect to the integral preceding it in the sequence.   We have

$$I_{k+1} = \int\limits_{k+1}^{k+2} (2n - z)(2n - 1 - z)\cdots(2 - z)\frac{(1 - z)z}{n - z}\, dz.$$

The substitution $z = 1 + u$ gives

$$I_{k+1} = \int\limits_k^{k+1} (2n - 1 - u)(2n - 2 - u)\cdots(1 - u)\frac{-u(1 + u)}{n - 1 - u}\, du$$

or

$$I_{k+1} = -\int\limits_k^{k+1} \frac{(1 + u)(n - u)}{(n - 1 - u)(2n - u)}$$

$$\times [(2n - u)(2n - 1 - u)\cdots(1 - u)]\frac{u\, du}{n - u},$$

and from this

$$| I_{k+1} | \leqq \int\limits_{k}^{k+1} \frac{(1 + u)(n - u)}{(n - 1 - u)(2n - u)} \, | (2n - u) \cdots (1 - u)| \, \frac{u \, du}{n - u} .$$

For $k \leqq u \leqq k + 1$ however

$$\frac{(1 + u)(n - u)}{(n - 1 - u)(2n - u)} < \frac{(k + 2)(n - k)}{(n - k - 2)(2n - k - 1)} ,$$

and hence

$$| I_{k+1} | < \frac{(k + 2)(n - k)}{(n - k - 2)(2n - k - 1)} \int\limits_{k}^{k+1} | (2n - u) \cdots (1 - u)| \, \frac{u \, du}{n - u} .$$

The product $(2n - u)(2n - 1 - u) \ldots (1 - u)$ has the sign $(-1)^k$ in the interval $[k, k + 1]$, since it contains exactly k negative factors $(k - u)$, $(k - 1 - u), \ldots, (1 - u)$. Hence

$$| (2n - u) \cdots (1 - u)| = (-1)^k (2n - u) \cdots (1 - u).$$

We thus obtain

$$| I_{k+1} | < \frac{(k + 2)(n - k)}{(n - k - 2)(2n - k - 1)} \, (-1)^k \int\limits_{k}^{k+1} (2n - u) \cdots (1 - u) \frac{u}{n - u} \, du.$$

The integral on the righthand side however is just the integral I_k, so that we have

$$| I_{k+1} | < \frac{(k + 2)(n - k)}{(n - k - 2)(2n - k - 1)} \, | I_k | ;$$

from this it follows that the ratio $\dfrac{I_{k+1}}{I_k}$ does indeed tend to zero with increasing n. Since therefore each of the integrals I_1, I_2, I_3, I_4 becomes arbitrary small with respect to I_0 as n increases, it follows that

$$I_1 + I_2 + I_3 + I_4 = \beta_n I_0 \qquad (\lim \beta_n = 0). \quad (247)$$

We must finally consider the integral I^*. To this end we direct our attention to the equation

$$\psi(z + 1) = (2n - 1 - z)(2n - 2 - z) \cdots (1 - z)(-z),$$

from which, together with (244), the functional equation

$$\frac{\psi(z+1)}{\psi(z)} = \frac{-z}{2n-z}$$

is obtained for $\psi(z)$; in another form:

$$\psi(z+1) = \frac{-z}{2n-z}\,\psi(z).$$

Now let M_k be the maximum value of $|\psi(z)|$ on the interval $[k, k+1]$. According to the functional equation, we then have

$$M_{k+1} < \frac{k+1}{2n-k-1}\,M_k. \tag{248}$$

If we here put $k = 0, 1, 2, 3, 4$ and multiply the inequalities so obtained, we find

$$M_5 < \frac{120}{(2n-1)(2n-2)(2n-3)(2n-4)(2n-5)}\,M_0.$$

From (244) however it is obvious that $M_0 = (2n)!$, so that

$$M_5 < \frac{K(2n)!}{n^5}, \tag{249}$$

where K is a constant independent of n.

On the other hand $k + 1 \leqq n - 1$, so that

$$\frac{k+1}{2n-k-1} \leqq \frac{n-1}{n+1} < 1.$$

From this and (248) it follows that

$$M_{k+1} < M_k \qquad\qquad (k \leqq n - 2).$$

Each of the quantities $M_6, M_7, \ldots, M_{n-1}$ therefore satisfies the same inequality (249) as M_5. On the entire interval $[5, n-1]$ therefore

$$|\psi(z)| < \frac{K(2n)!}{n^5},$$

and from this it follows that

$$|I^*| = \left| \int_5^{n-1} \psi(z)\,\frac{z\,dz}{n-z} \right| < K\,\frac{(2n)!}{n^5} \int_5^{n-1} \frac{z\,dz}{n-z}.$$

For $5 \leqq z \leqq n - 1$ however

$$0 < \frac{z}{n - z} \leqq \frac{n - 1}{n - (n - 1)} < n;$$

whence

$$|I^*| < K \frac{(2n)!}{n^3} = 2K \frac{(2n - 1)!}{n^2}.$$

Comparing this result with (246) we see that I^* also becomes arbitrarily small with respect to I_0:

$$I^* = \gamma_n I_0 \qquad\qquad (\lim \gamma_n = 0). \quad (250)$$

From (243), (245), (247), and (250) we obtain therefore

$$A_{n+1} = \alpha_n + \frac{(-1)^{n+1} 2}{n(n!)^2} (1 + \beta_n + \gamma_n) I_0,$$

where α_n, β_n, γ_n tend to zero with increasing n.

If n is so large that

$$|\alpha_n| < 1, \quad |\beta_n| < \frac{1}{4}, \quad |\gamma_n| < \frac{1}{4},$$

then (we recall that $I_0 > 0$) the inequality

$$|A_{n+1}| > \frac{1}{n(n!)^2} I_0 - 1$$

holds, and from (246) it follows that

$$|A_{n+1}| > \frac{(2n - 1)!}{6n^2(n!)^2} - 1.$$

Making use of STIRLING's formula [7]

$$n! = \sqrt{2\pi n}\, n^n e^{-n}(1 + \omega_n) \qquad\qquad (\lim \omega_n = 0)$$

we find

$$\frac{(2n - 1)!}{(n!)^2} = \frac{1}{2n} \frac{(2n)!}{(n!)^2} = \frac{1}{2n} \frac{\sqrt{4\pi n}\, (2n)^{2n} e^{-2n}}{2\pi n n^{2n} e^{-2n}} \frac{1 + \omega_{2n}}{(1 + \omega_n)^2} = \frac{2^{2n-1}}{\sqrt{\pi n^3}} (1 + \sigma_n)$$

where $\lim_{n \to \infty} \sigma_n = 0$. Hence

$$|A_{n+1}| > \frac{2^{2n-1}}{6n^3 \sqrt{\pi n}} (1 + \sigma_n) - 1,$$

[7] See Appendix 1 at the end of the book.

and therefore

$$\lim_{n \to \infty} |A_{n+1}| = +\infty,$$

wherewith the theorem is proved.

From this theorem it further follows that with equidistant nodes there must also be negative coefficients among the $A_k^{(n)}$. For this theorem establishes the existence of continuous functions for which the interpolation quadrature with equidistant nodes does not converge; the assertion therefore follows directly from the STEKLOV theorem.

§4. The TCHEBYSHEFF Problem and a BERNSTEIN Theorem

In addition to his research in pure mathematics, P. L. TCHEBYSHEFF devoted special attention to the requirements of computing practice. In so doing he was struck by the fact that in computing an integral by the quadrature formula

$$\int_a^b f(x)\, dx = \sum_{k=1}^n A_k f(x_k)$$

a total of n multiplications $A_k \times f(x_k)$ and $n-1$ additions are required; the computation thus becomes very arduous especially if—as is frequently the case—the coefficients A_k are accurate to a large number of decimal places. If all the coefficients A_k were equal, then the formula would assume the simple form

$$\int_a^b f(x)\, dx = A \sum_{k=1}^n f(x_k), \tag{251}$$

and the computation would still require $n-1$ additions as before, but now only a single multiplication must be performed.

The construction of a quadrature formula [8] of the form (251) would there-

---

[8] It might be of use to note that the HERMITE formula (220) is not related to this question. In order to compute the integral $I = \int_{-1}^{+1} F(x)\, dx$ by formula (220), we must first bring it to the form $I = \int_{-1}^{+1} f(x) \dfrac{dx}{\sqrt{1-x^2}}$, i.e. introduce the function $f(x) = F(x)\sqrt{1-x^2}$. The righthand side of formula (220) hence becomes $\dfrac{\pi}{n} \sum_{k=1}^n F(x_k)\sqrt{1-x_k^2}$ so that the unequal numbers $\dfrac{\pi}{n}\sqrt{1-x_k^2}$ appear as the quadrature coefficients.

fore be of special interest. Of course, such a formula would be worthless if it failed to provide satisfactory accuracy (at least for "well-behaved" functions). It is therefore natural to require that formula (251) should be exact for polynomials of highest possible degree.

It is hereby only necessary to construct such a formula for the interval $[-1, +1]$, since any other interval may be linearly mapped onto this one.

If the formula

$$\int\limits_{-1}^{+1} f(x)\, dx = A \sum_{k=1}^{n} f(x_k) \tag{252}$$

is to be exact for every polynomial in H_m, then it is clearly necessary and sufficient that it be exact for every power $f(x) = x^r$ $(r = 0, 1, 2, \ldots, m)$, i.e. that the $m + 1$ conditions

$$A \sum_{k=1}^{n} x_k^r = \int\limits_{-1}^{+1} x^r\, dx \tag{253}$$

be satisfied.

Since we have a total of $n + 1$ parameters $A, x_1, x_2, \ldots, x_n$ at our disposal, the most natural requirement is that $m = n$.

These considerations led P. L. TCHEBYSHEFF [4] to pose the following problem: *given n to determine the coefficient A and the nodes $x_1, x_2, \ldots, x_n$ such that formula* (252) *be exact for every polynomial in H_n.*

According to what has been said, in order to solve this problem we must solve the $n + 1$ equations (253). The special case $r = 0$ gives

$$A = \frac{2}{n}. \tag{254}$$

The other quantities $x_1, x_2, \ldots, x_n$ must be calculated from the remaining n equations (253) which form a nonlinear system. TCHEBYSHEFF gave the solution of the system for the cases $n = 1, 2, 3, 4, 5, 6, 7$.

In the case $n = 1$ we have only one equation

$$2x_1 = \int\limits_{-1}^{+1} x\, dx = 0,$$

whence it follows that $x_1 = 0$, and the TCHEBYSHEFF formula assumes the form

$$\int\limits_{-1}^{+1} f(x)\, dx = 2f(0)$$

In the case $n = 2$ we obtain the system of equations

$$x_1 + x_2 = \int\limits_{-1}^{+1} x\, dx = 0,$$

$$x_1^2 + x_2^2 = \int\limits_{-1}^{+1} x^2\, dx = \frac{2}{3}.$$

From these one obtains $-x_1 = x_2 = \dfrac{\sqrt{3}}{3} = 0.5773503$, and the TCHEBYSHEFF formula reads

$$\int\limits_{-1}^{+1} f(x)\, dx = f\left(-\frac{\sqrt{3}}{3}\right) + f\left(-\frac{\sqrt{3}}{3}\right).$$

In the case $n = 3$ the system of equations is

$$x_1 + x_2 + x_3 = 0,$$
$$x_1^2 + x_2^2 + x_3^2 = 1,$$
$$x_1^3 + x_2^3 + x_3^3 = 0.$$

By eliminating x_3 from the first and third equations one obtains

$$x_1 x_2 (x_1 + x_2) = 0.$$

Hence $x_1 x_2 x_3 = 0$.   Suppose $x_2 = 0$.   This gives

$$-x_1 = x_3 = \frac{\sqrt{2}}{2} = 0.7071068,$$

and the TCHEBYSHEFF formula takes the form

$$\int\limits_{-1}^{+1} f(x)\, dx = \frac{2}{3}\left[f\left(-\frac{\sqrt{2}}{2}\right) + f(0) + f\left(\frac{\sqrt{2}}{2}\right)\right].$$

We finally give the solution for $n = 4$.   The system of equations is

$$\left.\begin{aligned}
x_1 + x_2 + x_3 + x_4 &= 0, \\[2mm]
x_1^2 + x_2^2 + x_3^2 + x_4^2 &= \frac{4}{3}, \\[2mm]
x_1^3 + x_2^3 + x_3^3 + x_4^3 &= 0, \\[2mm]
x_1^4 + x_2^4 + x_3^4 + x_4^4 &= \frac{4}{5}.
\end{aligned}\right\} \tag{255}$$

We first note that none of the unknowns has the value zero.   If for example $x_4 = 0$, then one would obtain—as above—from the first three equations the solution $x_1 = -\sqrt{\frac{2}{3}}$, $x_2 = 0$, $x_3 = \sqrt{\frac{2}{3}}$ which does not satisfy the fourth equation.

Now four nonzero quantities cannot have pairwise different signs; we may therefore assume that two unknowns, say x_1 and x_2, have the same sign such that $x_1 + x_2 \neq 0$. We now bring the first equation to the form

$$x_1 + x_2 = -(x_3 + x_4), \tag{256}$$

raise it to the third power, and combine it with the third equation. We hereby obtain

$$(x_1 + x_2)(x_1 x_2 - x_3 x_4) = 0,$$

whence $x_1 x_2 = x_3 x_4$, so that x_3 and x_4 also have the same sign. We take x_1 and x_2 to be negative and x_3 and x_4 to be positive.

Squaring equation (256) and making use of $x_1 x_2 = x_3 x_4$, it is evident that

$$x_1^2 + x_2^2 = x_3^2 + x_4^2. \tag{257}$$

From this and the second equation of (255) it follows that

$$x_1^2 + x_2^2 = \frac{2}{3}. \tag{258}$$

Squaring equation (257) and combining the result with the fourth equation of (255), we obtain

$$x_1^4 + x_2^4 = \frac{2}{5}.$$

From this and (258) it follows that if $x_1 < x_2$ then

$$x_1 = -\sqrt{\frac{\sqrt{5}+2}{3\sqrt{5}}} = -0.7946544,$$

$$x_2 = -\sqrt{\frac{\sqrt{5}-2}{3\sqrt{5}}} = -0.1875925.$$

Similarly we find $x_3 = -x_2$, $x_4 = -x_1$. For $n = 4$ therefore the TCHEBY-SHEFF formula reads

$$\int_{-1}^{+1} f(x)\,dx = \frac{1}{2}\left[f\left(-\sqrt{\frac{\sqrt{5}+2}{3\sqrt{5}}}\right) + f\left(-\sqrt{\frac{\sqrt{5}-2}{3\sqrt{5}}}\right) \right.$$
$$\left. + f\left(\sqrt{\frac{\sqrt{5}-2}{3\sqrt{5}}}\right) + f\left(\sqrt{\frac{\sqrt{5}+2}{3\sqrt{5}}}\right) \right].$$

As already remarked, TCHEBYSHEFF computed the nodes for his formula for the cases $n = 5, 6, 7$ as well.   However, when after his work was published the solution for $n = 8$ was carried through, imaginary values were obtained. S. N. BERNSTEIN thereupon investigated the problem in detail. By means of remarkably elegant methods, he succeeded in proving that the TCHEBY-SHEFF problem is unsolvable for $n > 9$. We shall now present this proof.

Lemma 1.   *Suppose the formula*

$$\int_{-1}^{+1} f(x)\, dx = A \sum_{k=1}^{n} f(x_k) \tag{259}$$

is exact for all polynomials in H_{2m-1} where $m < n$; further let $X_m(x)$ be the LEGENDRE *polynomial of degree m and $\xi_1^{(m)}$ be its smallest root.   If the nodes x_k are enumerated in an increasing sequence, then*

$$x_1 < \xi_1^{(m)}.$$

Proof.   We set

$$P(x) = \frac{X_m^2(x)}{x - \xi_1^{(m)}}.$$

Since the polynomial $\dfrac{X_m(x)}{x - \xi_1^{(m)}}$ is of degree $m - 1$, it is orthogonal to $X_m(x)$; we therefore have

$$\int_{-1}^{+1} P(x)\, dx = 0.$$

Now $P(x)$ is of degree $2m - 1$, and the preceding integral may therefore be computed by means of formula (259), whence it follows that

$$\sum_{k=1}^{n} P(x_k) = 0.$$

Here not all summands can be equal to zero, since $P(x)$ has only m distinct roots and $n > m$.   Therefore there also exist negative summands.   But now $P(x) < 0$ only for $x < \xi_1^{(m)}$. There therefore exists at least one k such that $x_k < \xi_1^{(m)}$; hence for the smallest node x_1 it follows *a fortiori* that $x_1 < \xi_1^{(m)}$.

The following is based on combining the TCHEBYSHEFF formula (259) with the GAUSS formula

$$\int_{-1}^{+1} f(x)\, dx = \sum_{k=1}^{m} A_k^{(m)} f(\xi_k^{(m)}), \tag{260}$$

the nodes in which are the roots of the LEGENDRE polynomial.

Lemma 2.   *If the* TCHEBYSHEFF *formula*

$$\int_{-1}^{+1} f(x)\,dx = \frac{2}{n}\sum_{k=1}^{n} f(x_k) \tag{261}$$

is exact for all polynomials in H_{2m-1} where $m < n$, then

$$\frac{2}{n} < A_1^{(m)}. \tag{262}$$

Proof.   We set

$$P(x) = \left[\frac{X_m(x)}{X_m'(\xi_1^{(m)})(x - \xi_1^{(m)})}\right]^2.$$

This is a polynomial of degree $2m - 2$.   The integral

$$\int_{-1}^{+1} P(x)\,dx$$

can therefore be computed exactly by both the TCHEBYSHEFF formula (261) and the GAUSS formula (260).[9]   Computation with the former gives

$$\int_{-1}^{+1} P(x)\,dx = \frac{2}{n}\sum_{k=1}^{n} P(x_k),$$

and with the latter

$$\int_{-1}^{+1} P(x)\,dx = A_1^{(m)},$$

since $P(\xi_k^{(m)}) = 0$ for $k > 1$ and $P(\xi_1^{(m)}) = 1$.   Hence

$$\frac{2}{n}\sum_{k=1}^{n} P(x_k) = A_1^{(m)}.$$

Since the polynomial $P(x)$ is non-negative it thus follows that

$$\frac{2}{n} P(x_1) \leqq A_1^{(m)}. \tag{263}$$

The polynomial $P(x)$ has the double roots $\xi_2^{(m)}$, $\xi_3^{(m)}$, ..., $\xi_m^{(m)}$.   These $m - 1$ points are therefore also roots of its derivative $P'(x)$.   In addition to these roots, the polynomial $P'(x)$ according to ROLLE's theorem has $m - 2$ other roots in the intervals $(\xi_2^{(m)}, \xi_3^{(m)})$, ..., $(\xi_{m-1}^{(m)}, \xi_m^{(m)})$.   The interval $[\xi_2^{(m)}, \xi_m^{(m)}]$

---

[9] We recall that GAUSS's formula holds exactly for all polynomials in H_{2m-1}.

and hence the interval $[\xi_1^{(m)}, \xi_m^{(m)}]$ contains $2m - 3$ roots of $P'(x)$. But now $P'(x)$ is a polynomial of degree exactly $2m - 3$. For $x < \xi_1^{(m)}$ therefore $P'(x)$ has no roots, so that $P'(x)$ does not change sign in the interval $(-\infty, \xi_1^{(m)})$. Since moreover the degree of $P'(x)$ is odd, this sign is negative ($\lim\limits_{x \to -\infty} P'(x) = -\infty$). The function $P(x)$ therefore *decreases* in this interval. From Lemma 1 $x_1 < \xi_1^{(m)}$. Hence $P(x_1) > P(\xi_1^{(m)}) = 1$. Putting this result into (263) we obtain (262).

Theorem (S. N. BERNSTEIN [11, 12]).   *The* TCHEBYSHEFF *problem is unsolvable for* $n > 9$.

Proof.   The proof of this theorem follows very simply from the two preceding lemmas and two estimates found by BERNSTEIN:

$$A_1^{(m)} < \frac{\pi}{m} \sqrt{1 - [\xi_1^{(m)}]^2}, \tag{264}$$

$$-1 < \xi_1^{(m)} < -1 + \frac{3}{m(m + 1)} \qquad (m > 6). \tag{265}$$

For $m > 6$ it follows easily from these two estimates that

$$A_1^{(m)} < \frac{\pi\sqrt{6}}{m^2}. \tag{266}$$

We now assume that the TCHEBYSHEFF problem is solvable from some $n > 11$ and consider first the case where n is odd, i.e. $n = 2m - 1$.

From Lemma 2, formula (262) then applies; but since $m > 6$, it follows from (266) and (262) that

$$\frac{2}{n} < \frac{4\pi\sqrt{6}}{(n + 1)^2}.$$

Hence $(n + 1)^2 < 16n$ or

$$n^2 - 14n + 1 < 0,$$

so that n lies between the roots of the trinomial $x^2 - 14x + 1$. The larger of these roots is

$$7 + \sqrt{48} < 14,$$

and hence $n \leqq 13$. We now assume that with an appropriate choice of nodes the TCHEBYSHEFF formula is exact for $n = 13$. In this case $m = 7$, and according to (262)

$$\frac{2}{13} < A_1^{(7)}. \tag{267}$$

As previously mentioned, the coefficient $A_1^{(7)}$ was computed by GAUSS. It has the value

$$A_1^{(7)} = 0.12958\dots, \tag{268}$$

while

$$\frac{2}{13} = 0.153\dots;$$

estimate (267) is therefore incorrect. This means however that a TCHEBY-SHEFF formula is impossible for $n = 13$. The same reasoning leads in the case $n = 11$ to the contradictory relations

$$A_1^{(6)} = 0.17132 < \frac{2}{11}. \tag{269}$$

The greatest odd number for which a TCHEBYSHEFF formula exists is therefore $n = 9$ (that it in fact exists for $n = 9$ was proved after TCHEBYSHEFF's work).

We now investigate the even values of n. We assume that the system of equations

$$\left.\begin{aligned}
x_1 + x_2 + \cdots + x_n &= 0, \\
x_1^2 + x_2^2 + \cdots + x_n^2 &= \frac{n}{3}, \\
x_1^3 + x_2^3 + \cdots + x_n^3 &= 0, \\
\cdots\cdots\cdots\cdots\cdots \\
x_1^{n-1} + x_2^{n-1} + \cdots + x_n^{n-1} &= 0, \\
x_1^n + x_2^n + \cdots + x_n^n &= \frac{n}{n+1}
\end{aligned}\right\} \tag{270}$$

be solvable in such a manner that all the values x_i of the solution set are real, pairwise distinct, and lie in the interval $[-1, +1]$. If we order them $x_1 < x_2 < \cdots < x_n$, then this solution set is *uniquely* determined by (270). For from a theorem in algebra the equation whose roots are the numbers x_i is uniquely determined if the power sums

$$\sum_{i=1}^{n} x_i^k = s_k \qquad (k = 1, 2, \dots, n)$$

are given. In other words: the power sums s_k first determine the set of the numbers x_i uniquely and then the condition $x_1 < x_2 < \cdots < x_n$ specifies each x_i uniquely. On the other hand, if n is even the system (270) obviously has the solution $(-x_1, -x_2, \dots, -x_n)$ in addition to the solution $(x_1, x_2, \dots, x_n)$. But from this it follows that

$$x_1 = -x_n, \; x_2 = -x_{n-1}, \; \ldots, \; x_{\frac{n}{2}} = -x_{\frac{n}{2}+1},$$

and hence

$$x_1^{n+1} + x_2^{n+1} + \cdots + x_n^{n+1} = 0.$$

If therefore n is even and if the equation

$$\int_{-1}^{+1} x^r \, dx = \frac{2}{n} \sum_{k=1}^{n} x_k^r$$

holds for $r = 0, 1, 2, \ldots, n$, then it automatically holds for $r = n + 1$.

It has hence been proved that if n is an even number and if the TCHEBY-SHEFF formula with n nodes holds for all polynomials in H_n, then it holds automatically for all polynomials in H_{n+1}. Having established this, we assume that the TCHEBYSHEFF problem has a solution for an even number $n > 10$. If we set $2m - 1 = n + 1$ we obtain according to (262) and (266)

$$\frac{2}{n} < \frac{4\pi\sqrt{6}}{(n+2)^2}.$$

From this it follows that $(n + 2)^2 < 16n$ and

$$n^2 - 12n + 4 < 0.$$

Since now the greater of the two roots of the trinomial $x^2 - 12x + 4$ is equal to

$$6 + \sqrt{32} < 12,$$

this implies that $n \leqq 10$. This completes the proof that the TCHEBYSHEFF problem for $n > 10$ is unsolvable. For $n = 10$ it is also unsolvable since

$$A_1^{(6)} < \frac{1}{5}.$$

The proof just completed was of course based on the two inequalities (264) and (265) which we have not yet proved. The proof of (265) is relatively simple. We write $x^2 - 1$ in the form

$$x^2 - 1 = (x + 1)^2 - 2(x + 1)$$

and obtain with the help of the binomial formula

$$(x^2 - 1)^n = \sum_{k=0}^{n} C_n^k (-2)^{n-k} (x + 1)^{n+k}.$$

From this it follows that

$$[(x^2 - 1)^n]^{(n)}$$
$$= (-2)^n \sum_{k=0}^{n} (-1)^k (n + k)(n + k - 1) \cdots (k + 1) C_n^k \left(\frac{x + 1}{2}\right)^k.$$

Since the LEGENDRE polynomials are defined only up to a constant factor, we may put

$$X_n(x) = \sum_{k=0}^{n} (-1)^k (n+k)(n+k-1)\cdots(k+1) C_n^k \left(\frac{x+1}{2}\right)^k.$$

This gives $X_n(-1) = n!$. On the other hand

$$X_n\left(-1 + \frac{3}{n(n+1)}\right)$$

$$= \sum_{k=0}^{n} (-1)^k (n+k)(n+k-1)\cdots(k+1) C_n^k \left[\frac{3}{2n(n+1)}\right]^k.$$

Holding n fixed and setting

$$u_k = C_n^k (n+k)\cdots(k+1)\left[\frac{3}{2n(n+1)}\right]^k,$$

we find

$$\frac{u_k}{u_{k-1}} = \frac{3}{2}\frac{(n+k)(n-k+1)}{k^2 n(n+1)} = \frac{3}{2}\frac{1 - \dfrac{k(k-1)}{n(n+1)}}{k^2}, \qquad (271)$$

whence it is seen that the quotient $\dfrac{u_k}{u_{k-1}}$ decreases if k increases.

Since $u_k > 0$ and

$$X_n\left(-1 + \frac{3}{n(n+1)}\right) = \sum_{k=0}^{n} (-1)^k u_k,$$

it is evident that

$$X_n\left(-1 + \frac{3}{n(n+1)}\right) < (u_0 - u_1 + u_2 - u_3) + (u_4 + u_6 + u_8 + \cdots).$$

We compute $u_0 - u_1 + u_2 - u_3$ separately. This sum equals

$$-n!\left[\frac{1}{32} + \frac{3}{8n(n+1)} + \frac{9}{8n^2(n+1)^2}\right].$$

For all n therefore

$$u_0 - u_1 + u_2 - u_3 < -\frac{n!}{32}.$$

Since on the other hand $\dfrac{u_k}{u_{k-1}}$ decreases, we have

$$\frac{u_{2k}}{u_{2k-2}} = \frac{u_{2k}}{u_{2k-1}}\frac{u_{2k-1}}{u_{2k-2}} > \frac{u_{2k+2}}{u_{2k+1}}\frac{u_{2k+1}}{u_{2k}} = \frac{u_{2k+2}}{u_{2k}},$$

and hence

$$\frac{u_6}{u_4} > \frac{u_8}{u_6} > \frac{u_{10}}{u_8} > \cdots.$$

From this follows

$$\frac{u_8}{u_4} = \frac{u_8}{u_6} \cdot \frac{u_6}{u_4} < \left(\frac{u_6}{u_4}\right)^2; \quad \frac{u_{10}}{u_4} < \left(\frac{u_6}{u_4}\right)^3; \dots;$$

$$u_4 + u_6 + u_8 + \cdots < u_4 \left[1 + \frac{u_6}{u_4} + \left(\frac{u_6}{u_4}\right)^2 + \cdots\right] = \frac{u_4}{1 - \dfrac{u_6}{u_4}}.$$

According to (271) [10]

$$\frac{u_6}{u_4} = \frac{9}{4} \frac{1 - \dfrac{30}{n(n+1)}}{6^2} \frac{1 - \dfrac{20}{n(n+1)}}{5^2} < \frac{1}{400}.$$

Again on the basis of (271) we further obtain

$$u_4 = \frac{81}{16} \frac{1 - \dfrac{12}{n(n+1)}}{4^2} \frac{1 - \dfrac{6}{n(n+1)}}{3^2} \frac{1 - \dfrac{2}{n(n+1)}}{2^2} \frac{1}{1^2} n! < \frac{9n!}{1024},$$

and hence

$$\frac{u_4}{1 - \dfrac{u_6}{u_4}} < \frac{9n!}{1024 \cdot \dfrac{399}{400}} = \frac{75n!}{8512}.$$

Combining these results we therefore have

$$X_n\left(-1 + \frac{3}{n(n+1)}\right) < n!\left[\frac{75}{8512} - \frac{1}{32}\right] < 0.$$

But this means that $X_n(x)$ changes sign between -1 and $-1 + \dfrac{3}{n(n+1)}$, wherewith (265) is proved.

It remains to prove (264). To this end, we make use of the LEGENDRE polynomial

$$P_m(x) = \frac{1}{(2m)!!} \frac{d^m (x^2 - 1)^m}{dx^m}$$

and set

$$\varphi(\theta) = \sqrt{\sin \theta}\, P_m(\cos \theta). \tag{272}$$

Then

$$\varphi''(\theta) = \frac{4 \sin^4 \theta\, P_m''(\cos \theta) - 8 \sin^2 \theta \cos \theta\, P_m'(\cos \theta) - (1 + \sin^2 \theta)\, P_m(\cos \theta)}{4\sqrt{\sin^3 \theta}}.$$

[10] We recall that $n > 6$.

Now the LEGENDRE polynomial $P_m(x)$ satisfies the differential equation

$$(1 - x^2)y'' - 2xy' + m(m + 1)y = 0.$$

If we here substitute $P_m(x)$ and replace x by $\cos \theta$, we obtain after multiplication by $4 \sin^2 \theta$

$$4 \sin^4 \theta P_m''(\cos \theta) - 8 \sin^2 \theta \cos \theta P_m'(\cos \theta) = -4m(m + 1) \sin^2 \theta P_m(\cos \theta).$$

Using this and (272) our expression becomes

$$\varphi''(\theta) = - \frac{(2m + 1)^2 \sin^2 \theta + 1}{4 \sin^2 \theta} \varphi(\theta).$$

Putting

$$\lambda(\theta) = \frac{2 \sin \theta}{\sqrt{(2m + 1)^2 \sin^2 \theta + 1}},$$

the preceding equation becomes

$$\lambda^2(\theta)\varphi''(\theta) + \varphi(\theta) = 0. \tag{273}$$

Having established this, we introduce the function

$$u(\theta) = \varphi^2(\theta) + \lambda^2(\theta)\varphi'^2(\theta).$$

Differentiating this function and taking note of (273), we obtain

$$u'(\theta) = 2\lambda(\theta)\lambda'(\theta)\varphi'^2(\theta).$$

But now

$$2\lambda(\theta)\lambda'(\theta) = \frac{8 \sin \theta \cos \theta}{[(2m + 1)^2 \sin^2 \theta + 1]^2};$$

hence for $\frac{\pi}{2} < \theta < \pi$

$$2\lambda(\theta)\lambda'(\theta) < 0.$$

On the other hand it obviously follows from the definition of $u(\theta)$ that

$$u(\theta) \geqq \lambda^2(\theta)\varphi'^2(\theta),$$

and hence

$$\frac{2\lambda(\theta)\lambda'(\theta)}{\lambda^2(\theta)} u(\theta) \leqq 2\lambda(\theta)\lambda'(\theta)\varphi'^2(\theta) = u'(\theta).$$

From this we obtain the inequality

$$\frac{u'(\theta)}{u(\theta)} \geqq \frac{2\lambda'(\theta)}{\lambda(\theta)} \qquad \left(\frac{\pi}{2} < \theta < \pi \right).$$

Integration of this inequality over the interval $\left[\dfrac{\pi}{2},\ \theta\right]$ gives

$$u(\theta) > \frac{u\left(\dfrac{\pi}{2}\right)}{\lambda^2\left(\dfrac{\pi}{2}\right)}\,\lambda^2(\theta).$$

Noting that

$$\varphi'(\theta) = \frac{\cos\theta}{2\sqrt{\sin\theta}}\,P_m(\cos\theta) - \sqrt{\sin^3\theta}\,P'_m(\cos\theta),$$

by evaluating the definition of $u(\theta)$ we find for $\dfrac{\pi}{2} < \theta < \pi$ the estimate

$$\sin\theta P_m^2(\cos\theta) + \lambda^2(\theta)\left[\frac{\cos\theta}{2\sqrt{\sin\theta}}\,P_m(\cos\theta) - \sqrt{\sin^3\theta}\,P'_m(\cos\theta)\right]^2$$

$$> \frac{u\left(\dfrac{\pi}{2}\right)}{\lambda^2\left(\dfrac{\pi}{2}\right)}\,\lambda^2(\theta).$$

We here replace θ by arc cos x. We then obtain for $-1 < x < 0$ the inequality

$$\sqrt{1 - x^2}\,P_m^2(x) + \lambda^2(\text{arc cos } x)$$

$$\times \left[\frac{x}{2\sqrt[4]{1 - x^2}}\,P_m(x) - \sqrt[4]{(1 - x^2)^3}\,P'_m(x)\right]^2 > \frac{u\left(\dfrac{\pi}{2}\right)}{\lambda^2\left(\dfrac{\pi}{2}\right)}\,\lambda^2(\text{arc cos } x).$$

We now substitute $x = \xi_1^{(m)}$. Since this number is a root of $P_m(x)$, we obtain

$$(1 - [\xi_1^{(m)}]^2)^{3/2}P_m'^2(\xi_1^{(m)}) > \frac{u\left(\dfrac{\pi}{2}\right)}{\lambda^2\left(\dfrac{\pi}{2}\right)}.$$

But now

$$\lambda^2\left(\frac{\pi}{2}\right) = \frac{2}{2m^2 + 2m + 1}$$

and

$$u\left(\frac{\pi}{2}\right) = P_m^2(0) + \frac{2}{2m^2 + 2m + 1}\,P_m'^2(0).$$

If m is an even number, then $P_m'(0) = 0$ and [11]

$$u\left(\frac{\pi}{2}\right) = P_m^2(0) = \left[\frac{(m-1)!!}{m!!}\right]^2.$$

According to the WALLIS formula (Vol. I, Ch. 10, § 3) we have for even m

$$\frac{m!!}{(m-1)!!} = \sqrt{m+\theta}\,\sqrt{\frac{\pi}{2}} \qquad\qquad (0 < \theta < 1);$$

therefore

$$\left[\frac{(m-1)!!}{m!!}\right]^2 > \frac{2}{\pi(m+1)},$$

and further

$$(1 - [\xi_1^{(m)}]^2)^{3/2} P_m'^2(\xi_1^{(m)}) > \frac{2m^2 + 2m + 1}{\pi(m+1)} > \frac{2m}{\pi}.$$

If m is an odd number, then $P_m(0) = 0$ and

$$u\left(\frac{\pi}{2}\right) = \frac{2}{2m^2 + 2m + 1} P_m'^2(0).$$

In Volume II (Chapter V, § 2) we have found the equation

$$(1 - x^2)P_m'(x) = mP_{m-1}(x) - mxP_m(x).$$

If we here substitute $x = 0$ we obtain

$$P_m'(0) = mP_{m-1}(0),$$

and hence

$$u\left(\frac{\pi}{2}\right) = \frac{2}{2m^2 + 2m + 1} m^2 \left[\frac{(m-2)!!}{(m-1)!!}\right]^2 = \frac{2m^2}{2m^2 + 2m + 1}\,\frac{2}{(m-1+\theta)\pi};$$

from this follows

$$u\left(\frac{\pi}{2}\right) > \frac{4m}{(2m^2 + 2m + 1)\pi},$$

and further

$$(1 - [\xi_1^{(m)}]^2)^{3/2} P_m'^2(\xi_1^{(m)}) > \frac{2m}{\pi}.$$

---

[11] From the recursion formula (127) in Volume II we obtain for $x = 0$ and even n:

$$P_{n+2}(0) = -\frac{n+1}{n+2} P_n(0).$$

If one here substitutes $n = 0, 2, 4, \ldots, m - 2$ and multiplies all equations so obtained, one finds

$$P_m(0) = \pm \frac{(m-1)!!}{m!!} P_0(0) = \pm \frac{(m-1)!!}{m!!}.$$

This last inequality thus holds for all m; it may also be written in the form

$$\frac{\pi}{m} \sqrt{1 - [\xi_1^{(m)}]^2} > \frac{2}{1 - [\xi_1^{(m)}]^2} \frac{1}{P_m'^2(\xi_1^{(m)})}.$$

This formula together with (216) gives (264) immediately, wherewith the BERNSTEIN theorem has been completely proved.

Remark. The unsolvability of the TCHEBYSHEFF problem can only be caused by the existence of complex roots in the system

$$\sum_{k=1}^{n} x_k^r = \frac{n}{2} \int_{-1}^{+1} x^r \, dx \qquad (r = 0, 1, 2, \ldots, n). \quad (274)$$

For from a theorem of algebra it is possible, given an arbitrary power sum

$$s_r = \sum_{k=1}^{n} x_k^r \qquad (r = 0, 1, 2, \ldots, n),$$

to construct an algebraic equation having the numbers $x_1, x_2, \ldots, x_n$ as roots. From a purely algebraic viewpoint the system (274) therefore always has a solution. If n is an even number, then the last of the equations (274) reads

$$\sum_{k=1}^{n} x_k^n = \frac{n}{n+1}.$$

If all these numbers x_k are real, then they must all lie in the interval $[-1, +1]$, wherewith the TCHEBYSHEFF problem would be solved. The same consideration applies if n is odd, since in this case the next to the last equation in (274) reads

$$\sum_{k=1}^{n} x_k^{n-1} = 1.$$

The BERNSTEIN theorem therefore justifies the assertion that for $n > 9$ complex roots are to be found among the roots of the system (274). R. O. KUSMIN [2, 3] found a law for the distribution of these roots in the complex plane for sufficiently large values of n.

§ 5. The POSSE Theorem

We have already directed the reader's attention to the fact that the coefficients in the HERMITE quadrature formula

$$\int_{-1}^{+1} \frac{f(x)}{\sqrt{1 - x^2}} \, dx = \frac{\pi}{n} \sum_{k=1}^{n} f(x_k^{(n)}) \qquad \left(x_k^{(n)} = \cos \frac{2k - 1}{2n} \pi \right)$$

are independent of k. One might naturally ask if there are still other formulas of Gaussian type with this property. This question was answered negatively by K. A. POSSE [1] who proved that the HERMITE formula is the *only* one with this property. In this section we present the proof of the POSSE theorem due to J. L. GERONIMUS [6]. GERONIMUS proved the still more general

Theorem. *Let $p(x)$ be a weight function defined on the interval $[-1, +1]$, and let $x_k^{(n)}(k = 1, 2, \ldots, n)$ be the roots of a polynomial $\omega_n(x)$ which is orthogonal with weight $p(x)$ to all polynomials of H_{n-1}. If there exists a constant A_n for each n such that the formula*

$$\int_{-1}^{+1} p(x)x^m \, dx = A_n \sum_{k=1}^{n} [x_k^{(n)}]^m \qquad (275)$$

is exact for [12] $m = 0, 1, 2$, *then $p(x)$ is the TCHEBYSHEFF weight.*

Proof. For $m = 0$ formula (275) gives

$$\int_{-1}^{+1} p(x) \, dx = nA_n.$$

Without loss of generality we may put

$$\int_{-1}^{+1} p(x) \, dx = 1,$$

since one may multiply the weight function with an arbitrary constant factor. Hence

$$A_n = \frac{1}{n}.$$

For $m = 1$ (275) becomes

$$\frac{1}{n} \sum_{k=1}^{n} x_k^{(n)} = \mu_1 \qquad \left(\mu_1 = \int_{-1}^{+1} p(x)x \, dx \right).$$

If we write the polynomial $\omega_n(x)$, the leading coefficient of which we choose equal to one, in the form

$$\omega_n(x) = x^n + p_n x^{n-1} + q_n x^{n-2} + \cdots,$$

then from an elementary theorem of algebra

$$\sum_{k=1}^{n} x_k^{(n)} = -p_n,$$

and hence

$$p_n = -n\mu_1. \qquad (276)$$

[12] The value $m = 2$ enters the problem only if $n > 1$.

Comparing the coefficients of x^{n+1} in the recursion formula

$$\omega_{n+2}(x) = (x - \alpha_{n+2})\omega_{n+1}(x) - \lambda_{n+1}\omega_n(x) \quad (n \geqq 0), \quad (277)$$

we obtain

$$p_{n+2} = -\alpha_{n+2} + p_{n+1}$$

and similarly

$$p_{n+1} = -\alpha_{n+1} + p_n,$$
$$p_n = -\alpha_n + p_{n-1},$$
$$\cdots\cdots\cdots\cdots\cdots\cdots$$
$$p_2 = -\alpha_2 + p_1.$$

Addition of all these equations gives

$$p_{n+2} = -(\alpha_2 + \alpha_3 + \cdots + \alpha_{n+2}) + p_1.$$

But now $\omega_1(x) = x + p_1 = x - \alpha_1$. Hence

$$p_n = - \sum_{k=1}^{n} \alpha_k,$$

and therefore from (276)

$$\sum_{k=1}^{n} \alpha_k = n\mu_1.$$

Putting successively $n = 1, 2, 3, 4, \ldots$, we obtain

$$\alpha_1 = \alpha_2 = \alpha_3 = \alpha_4 = \cdots = \mu_1,$$

and we may therefore for brevity write α in place of α_k.

For $m = 2$ finally, formula (275) gives (where $n \geqq 2$)

$$\frac{1}{n} \sum_{k=1}^{n} [x_k^{(n)}]^2 = \mu_2 \qquad \left(\mu_2 = \int\limits_{-1}^{+1} p(x)x^2\, dx\right).$$

We now calculate the symmetric function

$$\sum_{k=1}^{n} [x_k^{(n)}]^2 = \left[\sum_{k=1}^{n} x_k^{(n)}\right]^2 - 2 \sum_{i<k} x_i^{(n)} x_k^{(n)} = p_n^2 - 2q_n;$$

hence

$$q_n = \frac{1}{2}[p_n^2 - n\mu_2] = \frac{n}{2}[n\mu_1^2 - \mu_2]. \quad (278)$$

Comparison of coefficients of x^n in (277) gives

$$q_{n+2} = -\alpha p_{n+1} + q_{n+1} - \lambda_{n+1}.$$

and similarly

$$q_{n+1} = -\alpha p_n + q_n - \lambda_n,$$
$$\cdots\cdots\cdots\cdots\cdots$$
$$q_3 = -\alpha p_2 + q_2 - \lambda_2,$$
$$q_2 = -\alpha p_1 - \lambda_1.$$

Adding all these equations we obtain

$$q_{n+2} = -\alpha \sum_{k=1}^{n+1} p_k - \sum_{k=1}^{n+1} \lambda_k.$$

Noting that $p_k = -k\alpha$, we have

$$q_n = \frac{n(n-1)}{2}\alpha^2 - \sum_{k=1}^{n-1} \lambda_k \qquad\qquad (n \geqq 2).$$

Comparing this formula with (278) gives

$$2\sum_{k=1}^{n-1} \lambda_k = n(\mu_2 - \mu_1^2).$$

If we here successively set $n = 2, 3, 4, \ldots$, we find that

$$\frac{\lambda_1}{2} = \lambda_2 = \lambda_3 = \lambda_4 = \cdots = \frac{1}{2}(\mu_2 - \mu_1^2).$$

If now [13]

$$\frac{1}{2}(\mu_2 - \mu_1^2) = \frac{\sigma^2}{4},$$

then

$$\lambda_1 = \frac{\sigma^2}{2}, \qquad \lambda_2 = \lambda_3 = \lambda_4 = \cdots = \frac{\sigma^2}{4}.$$

Recursion formula (277) therefore takes the forms

$$\omega_{n+2}(x) = (x - \alpha)\omega_{n+1}(x) - \frac{\sigma^2}{4}\omega_n(x) \qquad\qquad (n \geqq 1),$$

$$\omega_2(x) = (x - \alpha)\omega_1(x) - \frac{\sigma^2}{2}\omega_0(x),$$

where

$$\omega_0(x) = 1, \quad \omega_1(x) = x - \alpha.$$

[13] We recall that $\lambda_k > 0$!

For the TCHEBYSHEFF polynomials $\tilde{T}_n(x)$ we had

$$\tilde{T}_0(x) = 1, \quad \tilde{T}_1(x) = x,$$

$$\tilde{T}_2(x) = x\tilde{T}_1(x) - \frac{1}{2}\tilde{T}_0(x),$$

$$\tilde{T}_{n+2}(x) = x\tilde{T}_{n+1}(x) - \frac{1}{4}\tilde{T}_n(x). \qquad (n \geqq 1).$$

Comparing these formulas with those for $\omega_n(x)$, one obtains first of all

$$\omega_0(x) = \tilde{T}_0\left(\frac{x-\alpha}{\sigma}\right), \qquad \omega_1(x) = \sigma\tilde{T}_1\left(\frac{x-\alpha}{\sigma}\right).$$

From this it follows that

$$\omega_2(x) = (x-\alpha)\sigma\tilde{T}_1\left(\frac{x-\alpha}{\sigma}\right) - \frac{\sigma^2}{2}\tilde{T}_0\left(\frac{x-\alpha}{\sigma}\right)$$

$$= \sigma^2\left[\frac{x-\alpha}{\sigma}\tilde{T}_1\left(\frac{x-\alpha}{\sigma}\right) - \frac{1}{2}\tilde{T}_0\left(\frac{x-\alpha}{\sigma}\right)\right],$$

and hence

$$\omega_2(x) = \sigma^2\tilde{T}_2\left(\frac{x-\alpha}{\sigma}\right).$$

This procedure may be continued; by complete induction one obtains easily the equation

$$\omega_n(x) = \sigma^n\tilde{T}_n\left(\frac{x-\alpha}{\sigma}\right).$$

From this the roots of the polynomial $\omega_n(x)$ are seen to be the numbers

$$x_k^{(n)} = \alpha + \sigma\cos\frac{2k-1}{2n}\pi \qquad (k = 1, 2, \ldots, n).$$

The totality of these roots for $n = 1, 2, 3, \ldots$ forms an everywhere dense set in the interval $[\alpha - \sigma, \alpha + \sigma]$; this set contains no point outside the interval.

Now a quadrature formula of Gaussian type converges for every continuous function. By repeating literally the proof of the STEKLOV theorem in §1, we can convince ourselves that the totality of all nodes $x_k^{(n)}$ of such a quadrature must be dense in the interval $[-1, +1]$ and that no node may lie outside this interval.

We have therefore

$$\alpha - \sigma = -1, \quad \alpha + \sigma = 1,$$

whence it follows that $\alpha = 0$ and $\sigma = 1$; therefore

$$\omega_n(x) = \bar{T}_n(x).$$

In view of the fact that orthogonal polynomials determine their orthogonalizing weight on a finite interval uniquely, the proof of the theorem has herewith been completed.

APPENDIX I

Stirling's Formula

In the preceding chapters we have frequently made use of Stirling's formula

$$n! = \sqrt{2\pi n}\; n^n e^{-n}(1 + \omega_n) \qquad (\lim \omega_n = 0) \quad (279)$$

Since this formula is not always derived in analysis courses, we shall here present the proof of it. To this end, we investigate the function

$$x_n = \frac{n^n \sqrt{n}}{e^n n!}$$

defined on the natural numbers $n \geqq 1$. Our first objective will be to prove that x_n has a finite limit. To do this we must only show that x_n increases with increasing n but remains bounded. From

$$x_{n+1} = \frac{(n+1)^{n+1}\sqrt{n+1}}{e^{n+1}(n+1)!}$$

it follows that

$$\frac{x_{n+1}}{x_n} = \left(\frac{n+1}{n}\right)^{n+\frac{1}{2}}\frac{1}{e},$$

and hence

$$\ln \frac{x_{n+1}}{x_n} = \left(n + \frac{1}{2}\right)\ln\left(1 + \frac{1}{n}\right) - 1.$$

Now the hyperbola $xy = 1$ is a convex curve; the partially curved "trapezoid" formed by this hyperbola, the x axis, and the two lines $x = n$ and $x = n + 1$ parallel to the y axis is therefore bigger than the rectilinear trapezoid formed by the x axis, the same two parallel lines, and the tangent to the hyperbola at the point $\left(n + \frac{1}{2}, \frac{2}{2n+1}\right)$ (see Figure 1). Therefore

$$\int\limits_{n}^{n+1} \frac{dx}{x} > \frac{2}{2n+1},$$

156

whence it follows that

$$\left(n + \frac{1}{2}\right) \ln\left(1 + \frac{1}{n}\right) > 1,$$

so that we obtain

$$\ln \frac{x_{n+1}}{x_n} > 0.$$

The last inequality implies that $x_{n+1} > x_n$; the function is therefore increasing.

Figure 1

On the other hand, the curved trapezoid is smaller than the rectilinear trapezoid formed by the x axis, the same parallel lines, and the chord joining the points $\left(n, \frac{1}{n}\right)$ and $\left(n + 1, \frac{1}{n+1}\right)$. Hence

$$\int_n^{n+1} \frac{dx}{x} < \frac{1}{2}\left(\frac{1}{n} + \frac{1}{n+1}\right) = \frac{n + \frac{1}{2}}{n(n+1)},$$

and from this it follows that

$$\left(n + \frac{1}{2}\right) \ln\left(1 + \frac{1}{n}\right) < \frac{\left(n + \frac{1}{2}\right)^2}{n(n+1)} = 1 + \frac{1}{4n(n+1)}.$$

Therefore

$$\ln \frac{x_{n+1}}{x_n} < \frac{1}{4n(n+1)} = \frac{1}{4}\left(\frac{1}{n} - \frac{1}{n+1}\right). \tag{280}$$

If we here put $n = 1, 2, \ldots, m - 1$ and add the $m - 1$ inequalities so obtained, we find

$$\ln \frac{x_2}{x_1} + \ln \frac{x_3}{x_2} + \cdots + \ln \frac{x_m}{x_{m-1}}$$

$$< \frac{1}{4}\left[\left(1 - \frac{1}{2}\right) + \left(\frac{1}{2} - \frac{1}{3}\right) + \cdots + \left(\frac{1}{m-1} - \frac{1}{m}\right)\right],$$

and from this

$$\ln \frac{x_m}{x_1} < \frac{1}{4}\left(1 - \frac{1}{m}\right);$$

hence *a fortiori*

$$\ln \frac{x_n}{x_1} < \frac{1}{4},$$

and $x_n < x_1 \sqrt[4]{e}$. The x_n therefore have a limit which we denote by A:

$$A = \lim_{n \to \infty} \frac{n^n \sqrt{n}}{e^n n!}.$$

In Volume I, Chapter X, § 3 we derived the WALLIS formula

$$\frac{(2n)!!}{(2n-1)!!} = \sqrt{\pi n + \theta_n \pi} \qquad \left(0 < \theta_n < \frac{1}{2}\right).$$

Now

$$(2n)!! = 2^n n!, \quad (2n-1)!! = \frac{(2n)!}{(2n)!!} = \frac{(2n)!}{2^n n!}.$$

The WALLIS formula therefore assumes the form

$$\frac{2^{2n}(n!)^2}{(2n)!} = \sqrt{n\pi + \theta_n \pi}. \tag{281}$$

By definition of x_n

$$n! = \frac{n^n \sqrt{n}}{e^n x_n}, \quad (2n)! = \frac{(2n)^{2n}\sqrt{2n}}{e^{2n} x_{2n}},$$

wherewith (281) becomes

$$\frac{x_{2n}}{x_n^2}\sqrt{\frac{n}{2}} = \sqrt{n\pi + \theta_n \pi}.$$

Dividing both sides of this equation by $\sqrt{\dfrac{n}{2}}$ and passing to the limit, one obtains

$$\frac{A}{A^2} = \sqrt{2\pi},$$

whence $A = \dfrac{1}{\sqrt{2\pi}}$.   Therefore

$$\lim_{n \to \infty} \frac{n^n \sqrt{n}}{e^n n!} = \frac{1}{\sqrt{2\pi}},$$

and hence

$$\lim_{n \to \infty} \frac{\sqrt{2\pi n}\, n^n e^{-n}}{n!} = 1,$$

which is equivalent to formula (279).

Remark. It is not difficult to obtain an error estimate for STIRLING's formula; for from (280) it follows that

$$\ln \frac{x_{n+m}}{x_n} < \frac{1}{4}\left[\left(\frac{1}{n} - \frac{1}{n+1} \right) + \cdots + \left(\frac{1}{n+m-1} - \frac{1}{n+m} \right) \right]$$
$$= \frac{1}{4}\left(\frac{1}{n} - \frac{1}{n+m} \right).$$

If we here allow m to become arbitrarily large and pass to the limit, we find

$$\ln \frac{1}{\sqrt{2\pi}\, x_n} \leqq \frac{1}{4n},$$

whence

$$\frac{1}{\sqrt{2\pi}\, x_n} \leqq e^{\frac{1}{4n}}$$

and $\sqrt{2\pi}\, x_n \geqq e^{-\frac{1}{4n}}$. On the other hand the function x_n increases and remains less than its limit $A = \dfrac{1}{\sqrt{2\pi}}$; hence $\sqrt{2\pi}\, x_n < 1$.   We therefore have

$$e^{-\frac{1}{4n}} \leqq \frac{\sqrt{2\pi n}\, n^n e^{-n}}{n!} < 1$$

or

$$e^{-\frac{1}{4n}} \leqq \frac{1}{1+\omega_n} < 1,$$

whence it follows finally that

$$0 < \omega_n \leqq e^{\frac{1}{4n}} - 1.$$

APPENDIX 2

On the Müntz Theorems

For simplicity of presentation we restricted ourselves in the Müntz theorems (Volume II, Chapter III, § 3) to non-negative integral exponents n_i; such a restriction was by no means essential. We shall now investigate the problems posed by Müntz from a substantially more general point of view.

Let now $\{p_i\}$ be any sequence of real numbers subject only to the condition that $p_i > -\dfrac{1}{2}$ (we must impose this condition in order to ensure that the function x^{p_i} belong to $L^2([0, 1])$).

In exactly the same way as before, we can convince ourselves that the set of powers $\{x^{p_i}\}$ forms a fundamental system in $L^2([0, 1])$ if and only if for every non-negative, integral value m

$$\lim_{s \to \infty} \prod_{i=1}^{s} \frac{|p_i - m|}{m + p_i + 1} = 0. \tag{282}$$

If

$$\lim p_i = +\infty,$$

then it follows as previously that (282) is equivalent to the condition

$$\sum_{i=1}^{\infty} \frac{1}{p_i} = +\infty.$$

We now assume that a limit exists

$$\lim p_i = a \qquad \left(-\frac{1}{2} < a < +\infty \right).$$

In this case the set of powers $\{x^{p_i}\}$ is necessarily a fundamental system in $L^2([0, 1])$, since for every non-negative number m

$$-(m + a + 1) < a - m < m + a + 1,$$

and hence

$$\frac{|a - m|}{m + a + 1} < 1.$$

160

Choosing an arbitrary number q in the interval

$$\left(\frac{|a-m|}{a+m+1},\ 1\right),$$

we obtain for sufficiently large i the inequality

$$\frac{|p_i-m|}{m+p_i+1}<q,$$

whence (282) follows.

Finally we consider the case

$$\lim p_i=-\frac{1}{2}.$$

If we choose i_0 so large that for $i \geqq i_0$ the inequality $p_i < 0$ holds, then

$$\ln\prod_{i=i_0}^{s}\frac{m-p_i}{m+p_i+1}=\sum_{i=i_0}^{s}\ln\left(1-\frac{p_i+\frac{1}{2}}{m+\frac{1}{2}}\right)-\sum_{i=i_0}^{s}\ln\left(1+\frac{p_i+\frac{1}{2}}{m+\frac{1}{2}}\right).$$

From this it is evident that in this case condition (282) is equivalent to the condition

$$\sum_{i=1}^{\infty}\left(p_i+\frac{1}{2}\right)=+\infty.$$

From all this we obtain the

Theorem (CH. MÜNTZ). *A set of powers $\{x^p\}$ with $p > -\dfrac{1}{2}$ is a fundamental system if it is possible to select a sequence p_i from the set $\{p\}$ of exponents which is of one of the following three types:*

1. $\lim p_i=+\infty,$ $\qquad\qquad \sum\dfrac{1}{p_i}=+\infty\,;$

2. $\lim p_i=a,$ $\qquad\qquad -\dfrac{1}{2}<a<+\infty\,;$

3. $\lim p_i=-\dfrac{1}{2},$ $\qquad \sum\left(p_i+\dfrac{1}{2}\right)=+\infty\,.$

Otherwise $\{x^p\}$ is not a fundamental system.

Proof. Only the last assertion of the theorem still requires proof. We assume that the set $\{p\}$ contains no sequence of one of the three types. The set $\{p\}$ then has no accumulation point in the interval $\left(-\dfrac{1}{2}, +\infty\right)$ and is therefore at most countable: $\{p\} = \{p_i\}$. We partition this set into two parts A and B, putting all negative p_i in A and all non-negative p_i in B. Then [1] for $p_i \,\epsilon\, A$

$$\lim p_i = -\frac{1}{2}, \qquad \sum\left(p_i + \frac{1}{2}\right) < +\infty$$

and for $p_i \,\epsilon\, B$

$$\lim p_i = +\infty, \qquad\qquad \sum\frac{1}{p_i} < +\infty.$$

This means that the two infinite products

$$\prod_A \frac{|m - p_i|}{m + p_i + 1}, \qquad \prod_B \frac{|m - p_i|}{m + p_i + 1}$$

are nonzero, and hence that (282) is satisfied.

We now apply our questions in another direction and investigate what conditions a set of powers $\{x^p\}$ must satisfy in order that every function in $C([0, 1])$ can be approximated to arbitrary accuracy by linear combinations of powers contained in $\{x^p\}$. We need not hereby consider negative powers, since if such an exponent $p < 0$ occurred the "approximation polynomial" would become infinite at the point $x = 0$.

The following theorem contains a result in this direction which is essentially due to S. N. BERNSTEIN [2] who published it before MÜNTZ's work appeared.

Theorem. *Let $s = \{p\}$ be a set of non-negative real numbers. In order that the "polynomials"*

$$\sum_{k=1}^{n} c_k x^{p_k} \qquad\qquad (p_k \,\epsilon\, S)$$

form an everywhere dense set in $C([0, 1])$ it is sufficient that $p = 0$ belong to S and that in addition S satisfy one of the two following conditions:

1. *S contains a sequence $\{p_i\}$ such that*

$$\lim p_i = +\infty, \qquad \sum\frac{1}{p_i} = +\infty.$$

2. *S contains a convergent sequence $\{p_i\}$ such that*

$$0 < \lim p_i < +\infty.$$

---

[1] We suppose A and B are infinite; otherwise everything is trivial.
[2] S. N. BERNSTEIN [3]. BERNSTEIN's method of proof differs from ours.

Proof. The proof that condition 1 together with the requirement $0 \, \epsilon \, S$ is sufficient is completely analogous to the proof in the main text of the book.

If condition 2 is satisfied and such that

$$\lim p_i > \frac{1}{2},$$

then the set of powers $\{x^{p_i-1}\}$ is a fundamental system in $L^2([0, 1])$, whence the remainder of the proof follows easily.

If $p_i \leq \dfrac{1}{2}$ we choose a multiplier s such that $\lim sp_i > \dfrac{1}{2}$. From what has just been proved, the polynomials $\sum c_k x^{sp_k}$ form an everywhere dense set in $C([0, 1])$. Now let $f(x) \, \epsilon \, C([0, 1])$ and $\varphi(y) = f(y^s)$. This function also belongs to $C([0, 1])$, so that given $\varepsilon > 0$, coefficients c_k can be found such that

$$|\sum c_k y^{sp_k} - f(y^s)| < \varepsilon \qquad\qquad (0 \leq y \leq 1).$$

To complete the proof we have only to replace y^s by x.

APPENDIX 3

The Theorems of S. M. Losinski—F. I. Kharshiladze and V. F. Nikolaev

In § 4, Chapter IV, Volume II we mentioned a theorem due to V. F. Nikolaev according to which there does not exist an orthonormal system of polynomials with some weight function in terms of which every continuous function may be expanded into a uniformly convergent series. This result was presented by V. F. Nikolaev for the first time in a seminar at the University of Leningrad in which S. M. Losinski and F. I. Kharshiladze were also participating. Both the latter noted that the method of proof used by Nikolaev led to a much more general theorem. In this appendix we shall present their results.

We make the following agreement: if to every function $\varphi(x) \in C([a, b])$ there is made to correspond a function $\psi(x) \in C([a, b])$

$$\psi(x) = \psi[\varphi; x] = U(\varphi),$$

and if this correspondence satisfies in addition the conditions

$\alpha)$ $U(\varphi_1 + \varphi_2) = U(\varphi_1) + U(\varphi_2),$
$\beta)$ $\max |\psi(x)| \leqq K \max |\varphi(x)|,$

where the constant K does not depend on $\varphi(x)$, then $U(\varphi)$ shall be called a *"linear functional from the space $C([a, b])$ to the space $C([a, b])$"*.

It is easily seen that such a functional is *homogeneous*, i.e. for every constant c

$\gamma)$ $U(c\varphi) = cU(\varphi).$

The numbers K satisfying condition $\beta)$ are all non-negative and therefore possess a lower bound K_0 where K_0 obviously also satisfies condition $\beta)$. We shall call this number K_0 the *norm* of the functional $U(\varphi)$ and denote it by $\|U\|$.

Lemma 1. *Let $U_1(\varphi)$, $U_2(\varphi)$, $U_3(\varphi)$, ... be a sequence of linear functionals from $C([a, b])$ to $C([a, b])$. If for every function $\bar{\varphi}(x)$ the function corresponding to it*

$$\psi_n(x) = U_n(\varphi)$$

is bounded on $[a, b]$ by a number independent of n

$$|\psi_n(x)| \leqq A(\varphi) \qquad (a \leqq x \leqq b; \; n = 1, 2, 3, \ldots),$$

then the norms of the functionals $U_n(\varphi)$ are also bounded by a number independent of n.

Proof. We carry out the proof by the "sliding hump" method. To this end we assume that the norms of the functionals are not bounded and construct for every index n a function $\varphi_n(x)$ which satisfies the inequality [1]

$$\max |U_n(\overline{\varphi}_n)| > \frac{1}{2} \|U_n\| \max |\overline{\varphi}_n(x)|$$

If we put $2M_n = \|U_n\|$ and

$$\varphi_n(x) = \frac{\overline{\varphi}_n(x)}{\max |\overline{\varphi}_n(x)|},$$

then for all n

$$\max |U_n(\varphi_n)| > M_n, \quad \max |\varphi_n(x)| = 1,$$

where the set of numbers M_n is unbounded.

Having thus constructed the functions $\varphi_n(x)$, we now define an increasing sequence of indices $n_1 < n_2 < n_3 < \cdots$ in the following manner. Let $n_1 = 1$. We choose for n_2 a natural number such that

$$M_{n_2} > 3 \cdot 4^2 \left[A\left(\frac{\varphi_{n_1}}{4}\right) + 2 \right],$$

and then n_3 such that

$$M_{n_3} > 3 \cdot 4^3 \left[A\left(\frac{\varphi_{n_1}}{4} + \frac{\varphi_{n_2}}{4^2}\right) + 3 \right]$$

where in addition $n_3 > n_2$. Continuing this procedure, we arrive at a definition of n_m by the conditions

$$M_{n_m} > 3 \cdot 4^m \left[A\left(\sum_{k=1}^{m-1} \frac{\varphi_{n_k}}{4^k}\right) + m \right]$$

and $n_m > n_{m-1}$. This is the required sequence of indices.

We now set

$$\varphi(x) = \sum_{k=1}^{\infty} \frac{\varphi_{n_k}(x)}{4^k} ;$$

---

[1] For certain indices n it is possible that $\|U_n\| = 0$; these we leave out. For the others $\frac{1}{2}\|U_n\| < \|U_n\|$, so that a function $\overline{\varphi}_n(x)$ exists.

$\varphi(x)$ is clearly a continuous function. For all n therefore

$$| U_n(\varphi)| \leqq A(\varphi). \tag{283}$$

On the other hand

$$U_{n_m}(\varphi) = U_{n_m} \left(\sum_{k=1}^{m-1} \frac{\varphi_{n_k}(x)}{4^k} \right) + \frac{1}{4^m} U_{n_m}(\varphi_{n_m}) + U_{n_m} \left(\sum_{k=m+1}^{\infty} \frac{\varphi_{n_k}(x)}{4^k} \right).$$

By hypothesis

$$\left| U_{nm} \left(\sum_{k=1}^{m-1} \frac{\varphi_{n_k}}{4^k} \right) \right| \leqq A \left(\sum_{k=1}^{m-1} \frac{\varphi_{n_k}}{4^k} \right).$$

Moreover

$$\left| U_{n_m} \left(\sum_{k=m+1}^{\infty} \frac{\varphi_{n_k}}{4^k} \right) \right| \leqq \|U_{n_m}\| \max \left| \sum_{k=m+1}^{\infty} \frac{\varphi_{n_k}(x)}{4^k} \right| \leqq 2M_{nm} \sum_{k=m+1}^{\infty} \frac{1}{4^k} = \frac{2M_{nm}}{3 \cdot 4^m}.$$

For all $x \epsilon [a, b]$ therefore

$$| U_{n_m}(\varphi)| \geqq \frac{1}{4^m} | U_{n_m}(\varphi_{n_m})| - A \left(\sum_{k=1}^{m-1} \frac{\varphi_{n_k}}{4^k} \right) - \frac{2M_{nm}}{3 \cdot 4^m}.$$

According to the construction of the function $\varphi_{n_m}(x)$ however, it is possible to give a point $x_m \epsilon [a, b]$ at which

$$| U_{n_m}(\varphi_{n_m})| > M_{n_m}.$$

At this point then

$$| U_{n_m}(\varphi_{n_m})| > \frac{M_{n_m}}{3 \cdot 4^m} - A \left(\sum_{k=1}^{m-1} \frac{\varphi_{n_k}}{4^k} \right) > m,$$

which contradicts inequality (283).

Lemma 2. *Let $U_n(\varphi)$ be a linear functional from $C([0, \pi])$ to $C([0, \pi])$ with the following two properties:*

1. For every function $\varphi(x) \epsilon C([0, \pi])$ the functional $U_n(\varphi)$ is an even trigonometric polynomial in H_n^T.

2. If $T_n(x)$ is an even trigonometric polynomial in H_n^T, then

$$U_n(T_n) \equiv T_n(x).$$

The following inequality then holds:

$$\|U_n\| \geqq \frac{\ln n}{8\sqrt{\pi}}.$$

Proof.   We return to the polynomials

$$A(x) = \frac{\cos x}{n} + \frac{\cos 2x}{n-1} + \cdots + \frac{\cos nx}{1},$$

$$B(x) = \frac{\cos (n+2)x}{1} + \frac{\cos (n+3)x}{2} + \cdots + \frac{\cos (2n+1)x}{n},$$

which we have already studied in § 3, Chapter VII, Volume I where we found the inequality:

$$|A(x) - B(x)| \leqq 4\sqrt{\pi}.$$

Now let y be any constant and

$$Q_y(x) = U_n[B(x+y) + B(x-y)].$$

From

$$B(x+y) + B(x-y) = \sum_{k=n+2}^{2n+1} \frac{2 \cos kx \cos ky}{k-n-1}$$

we then have

$$Q_y(x) = \sum_{k=n+2}^{2n+1} V_k(x) \cos ky,$$

where for brevity we have set

$$V_k(x) = U_n\left(\frac{2 \cos kx}{k-n-1}\right).$$

It is important that $V_k(x)$ is of at most order n.   Hence

$$\int_0^\pi Q_y(y)\, dy = \frac{1}{2} \int_{-\pi}^\pi \left[\sum_{k=n+2}^{2n+1} V_k(y) \cos ky \right] dy = 0.$$

On the other hand, $A(2y)$ is a polynomial without constant term, and therefore

$$\int_0^\pi A(2y)\, dy = 0.$$

Hence

$$\int_0^\pi [A(2y) - Q_y(y)]\, dy = 0,$$

so that there is certainly a point a in $[0, \pi]$ at which

$$A(2a) - Q_a(a) = 0.$$

Having established this, we put

$$T(x) = [A(x + a) + A(x - a)] - [B(x + a) + B(x - a)].$$

It is obvious first of all that

$$|T(x)| \leqq 8\sqrt{\pi}.$$

If $V(x) = U_n(T)$, then

$$V(x) = A(x + a) + A(x - a) - Q_a(x),$$

and hence

$$V(a) = A(0) = \sum_{k=1}^{n} \frac{1}{k} > \ln n.$$

Therefore

$$\ln n < \max |V(x)| \leqq \|U_n\| \max |T(x)| \leqq 8\sqrt{\pi}\, \|U_n\|,$$

wherewith the lemma is proved.

Lemma 3. *Let $U_n(\varphi)$ be a linear functional that takes every function $\varphi(x) \in C([a, b])$ into an algebraic polynomial in H_n and which moreover takes every polynomial P_n in H_n into itself:*

$$U_n(P_n) \equiv P_n(x).$$

Then

$$\|U_n\| \geqq \frac{\ln n}{8\sqrt{\pi}}.$$

Proof. We make use of the unique map of $C([a, b])$ onto $C([0, \pi])$ whereby to every function $\varphi(x) \in C([a, b])$ is assigned the induced function

$$\bar{\varphi}(\theta) = \varphi\left[\frac{(b - a)\cos\theta + a + b}{2} \right].$$

In this mapping it is important that the sum $\bar{\varphi}_1 + \varphi_2$ correspond to the sum $\bar{\varphi}_1 + \bar{\varphi}_2$ and that $\max |\varphi(x)| = \max |\varphi(\theta)|$.

The class H_n, which is a subset of $C([a, b])$, is hereby mapped in one-to-one fashion onto the class of all even trigonometric functions in H_n^T.

Hence, choosing a function $\varphi(x) \in C([a, b])$ is the same as choosing its image function $\bar{\varphi}(x) \in C([0, \pi])$, and this holds in particular for the polynomials. Hence we may regard the functional U_n as being defined on $C([0, \pi])$;

it then possesses the properties 1 and 2 of Lemma 2.   The rest of the proof is obvious.

It is now not difficult to prove the theorem of LOSINSKI-KHARSHILADZE:

Theorem.   *There does not exist a sequence $\{U_n(\varphi)\}$ $(n = 1, 2, 3, \ldots)$ of linear functionals possessing all three of the following properties:*

1. $U_n(\varphi)$ *takes every function $\varphi \, \epsilon \, C([a, b])$ into a polynomial in H_n.*
2. *For every polynomial $P(x) \, \epsilon \, H_n$, $U_n(P) \equiv P(x)$.*
3. *For every function $\varphi(x) \, \epsilon \, C([a, b])$*

$$\lim_{n \to \infty} U_n(\varphi) = \varphi(x)$$

uniformly on $[a, b]$.

Proof.   If there were such a functional, then by Lemma 3 the sequence of norms would be unbounded while according to 3

$$|U_n(\varphi)| \leq A(\varphi)$$

for all n; this would imply by Lemma 1 that the sequence of norms were bounded.   This contradiction proves the theorem.

Recalling that the partial sums of a FOURIER expansion of a continuous function in terms of some system of orthogonal polynomials are linear functionals for which conditions 1 and 2 are satisfied, we see that the theorem of NIKOLAEV mentioned above is indeed a special case of the theorem just proved.

Finally, we remark that the FABER theorem can also be deduced from the theorem of LOSINSKI-KHARSHILADZE.

BIBLIOGRAPHY

BERMAN, D. L.
  [1] *Ob odnom interpolyatsionnom protsesse Ermita* (On a certain Hermite interpolation process). DAN, 1947

BERNSTEIN, S. N.
  [3] *Sur l'ordre de la meilleure approximation des fonctions continues par des polynômes de degré donné* (On the order of the best approximation of continuous functions by polynomials of given degree). Mem. Acad. de Belgique, 1912
  [6] *Quelques remarques sur l'interpolation* (Certain remarks on interpolation). Kharkov, Communications of the Mathematical Association, 1916
  [8] *Sur une modification de la formule d'interpolation de Lagrange* (On a modification of the Lagrange interpolation formula). Kharkov, Notices of the Mathematical Society, 1932
  [9] *O trigonometricheskom interpolirovanii po sposobu naimen'shikh kvadratov* (On trigonometric interpolation by the method of least squares). DAN, 1934
  [11] *O formulakh kvadratur Kotesa i Chebysheva* (On the quadrature formulas of Cotes and Tchebysheff). DAN, 1937
  [12] *Sur un système d'équations indtéerminées* (On a system of indeterminate equations). Journ. math. pur. et appl., 1938

BESIKOVICH, J. S.
  [1] *Ischislenie konechnykh raznostey* (Finite difference calculus). Leningrad, University Press, 1939

CHRISTOFFEL, E. B.
  [1] *Über die Gauss'sche Quadratur und eine Verallgemeinerung derselben* (On the Gauss quadrature and a generalization of the same). Journ. für Math., 1858

ERDÖS, P. and TURÁN, P.
  [1] *On interpolation. I.* Ann. of Math., 1937

FABER, G.
  [1] *Über die interpolatorische Darstellung stetiger Funktionen* (On the interpolatory representation of continuous functions). Jahresber. der DMV, 1914

170

FEJÉR, L.
  [2] *Über Interpolation* (On interpolation). Gött. Nachr., 1916
  [3] *Die Abschätzung eines Polynoms in einem Intervalle, wenn Schranken
      für seine Werte und ersten Ableitungswerte in einzelnen Punkten des
      Intervalles gegeben sind, und ihre Anwendung auf die Konvergenzfrage
      Hermitescher Interpolationsreihen* (Approximation of a polynomial in
      an interval when bounds for its values and the values of its first deriva-
      tive at certain points of the interval are given, and application to the
      question of convergence of Hermite interpolation series). Math. Z.,
      1930
  [4] *Lagrangesche Interpolation und die zugehörigen konjugierten Punkte* (La-
      grange interpolation and the corresponding conjugate points). Math.
      Ann., 1932
  [5] *Mechanische Quadraturen mit positiven Cotesschen Zahlen* (Mechanical
      quadratures with positive Cotes' numbers). Math. Z., 1933

FELDHEIM, E.
  [1] *O kharaktere skhodimosti pri interpolirovanii metodom Lagranzha* (On
      the nature of convergence when interpolating with the Lagrange
      method). DAN, 1937

GAUSS, C. F.
  [1] *Methodus nova integralium valores per approximationem inveniendi* (A
      new method of obtaining the value of integrals by approximation).
      Werke, Bd. 3

GERONIMUS, J. L.
  [6] *On Gauss' and Tchebysheff's quadrature formulas.* Bull. Amer. Math.
      Soc., 1944

GONCHAROV, V. L.
  [1] *Teoriya interpolirovanii i priblizheniya funktsiy* (Theory of interpola-
      tion and approximation of functions). Moscow-Leningrad GTTI, 1934

GRÜNWALD, G.
  [1] *Über Divergenzerscheinungen der Lagrangeschen Interpolationspolynome
      stetiger Funktionen* (On divergence of the Lagrange interpolation poly-
      nomials of continuous functions). Ann. of Math., 1936
  [2] *On the theory of interpolation.* Acta Math., 1943

GRÜNWALD, G. and TURÁN, P.
  [1] *Über Interpolation* (On interpolation). Ann. di Sc. Norm. di Pisa, 1938

HERMITE, CH.
  [2] *Sur la formule d'interpolation de Lagrange* (On the Lagrange interpola-
      tion formula. Journ. für Math., 1878

KHARSHILADZE, F. I.

[2] *Ob odnoy teoreme S. N. Bernshteyna iz teorii interpolyatsiy* (On a theorem of S. N. Bernstein in the theory of interpolation). Leningrad, Studies of the Inst. of Mech. and Optics, 1941

KOLMOGOROFF, A. N.

[1] *Une série de Fourier-Lebesgue divergente partout* (An everywhere divergent Fourier-Lebesgue series). C. R. Acad. Sci., 1926

KUSMIN, R. O.

[1] *K teorii mekhanicheskikh kvadratur* (On the theory of mechanical quadratures). Leningrad, Bull. Polyt. Inst., Dept. of Tech., Sci., and Math., 1931

[2] *Sur la méthode de Tchebycheff pour l'évaluation approchée des intégrales* (On the Tchebysheff method for the approximate evaluation of integrals). C. R. Acad. Sci., 1935

[3] *O raspredelenii korney polinomov, svyazannykh c kvadraturami Chebysheva* (On the distribution of roots of polynomials related to Tchebysheff quadratures). IAN, math. series, 1938

KUSMIN, R. O. and NATANSON, I. P.

[1] *O sil'noy skhodimosti interpolyatsionnogo polinoma Lagranzha* (On the strong convergence of Lagrange interpolation polynomials). Leningrad, Sci. Notices of the Univ., math. series, 1939

LOSINSKI, S. M.

[1] *O sil'noy skhodimosti interpolyatsionnykh protsessov* (On the strong convergence of interpolation processes). DAN, 1940

[2] *O sil'noy skhodimosti interpolyatsionnykh protsessov* (On the strong convergence of interpolation processes) DAN, 1941

[3] *On convergence and summability of Fourier series and interpolation processes.* Mat. Sb., 1944

[4] *Prostranstva $\tilde{C}\omega$ i $\tilde{C}_\omega^*$ i skhodimost' interpolyatsionnykh protsessov v nikh* (The spaces $\tilde{C}\omega$ and $\tilde{C}_\omega^*$ and convergence of interpolation processes therein). DAN, 1948

MARCINKIEWICZ, I.

[1] *Quelques remarkues sur l'interpolation* (Some remarks on interpolation). Acta Litterarum ac Scientiarum, Szeged, 1937

[2] *Sur la divergence des polynômes d'interpolation* (On the divergence of interpolation polynomials). Acta Litterarum ac Scientiarum, Szeged, 1937

MARKOFF, A. A.

[1] *O nekotorykh prilozheniyakh algebraicheskikh nepreryvnykh drobey* (On several applications of algebraic continued fractions). SPB, 1884

[2] *Sur la méthode de Gauss pour le calcul approché des integrales* (On the Gauss method of approximate calculation of integrals). Math. Ann., 1885

[4] *Ischislenie konechnykh raznostey* (Finite difference calculus). Odessa, 1892

NATANSON, I. P.

[6] *On the convergence of trigonometrical interpolation at equidistant knots.* Ann. of Math., 1944

POLYA, G.

[1] *Über die Konvergenz von Quadraturverfahren* (On the convergence of quadrature processes). Math. Z., 1933

POSSE, K. A.

[1] *Sur les quadratures* (On quadratures). Nouv. Ann. de Math., 1875

RAPPOPORT, S. I.

[1] *Ob odnom protsesse priblizheniya funktsiy trigonometricheskimi polinomami* (On a certain method of approximating functions by trigonometric polynomials). DAN, 1947

STEKLOV, V. A

[2] *O priblizhennom vychislenii opredelennykh integralov pri pomoshchi formul mekhanicheskikh kvadratur* (On the approximate calculation of particular integrals by means of formulas for mechanical quadratures). IAN, 1916

STIELTJES, T. J.

[1] *Quelques recherches sur la théorie des quadratures dites mécaniques* (Certain investigations in the theory of so-called mechanical quadratures). Ann. de L'Éc. Norm., 1884

SZEGÖ, G.

[1] *Orthogonal polynomials.* Amer. Math. Soc. Colloq. Pub., 1939

TCHEBYSHEFF, P. L.

[4] *O kvadraturakh* (On quadratures). Complete Works (1873).

ZYGMUND, A.

[1] *Trigonometricheskie ryady* (Trigonometric series). Moscow-Leningrad, 1939

INDEX

INDEX OF SYMBOLS